REEF FIS
AND CORAL

The Red Sea

PETE HARRISON & ALEX MISIEWICZ

First published in 2000 by
New Holland Publishers (UK) Ltd
London • Cape Town • Sydney • Auckland
www.newhollandpublishers.com

Garfield House, 86–88 Edgware Road
London W2 2EA, United Kingdom

80 McKenzie Street
Cape Town 800, South Africa

14 Aquatic Drive, Frenchs Forest
NSW 2086, Australia

218 Lake Road, Northcote
Auckland, New Zealand

10 9 8 7 6 5 4 3

ISBN 1 85974 207 6

Commissioning Editor: Jo Hemmings
Assistant Editor: Michaella Standen
Editing and design: D & N Publishing, Hungerford, Berkshire

Reproduction by Modern Age Repro House Limited, Hong Kong
Printed and bound in Singapore by Kyodo Printing Co (Singapore) Pte Ltd

Photographer's Acknowledgements

Amanda Levick of Oonasdivers
Rolf and Petra at Sinai Divers
Hesham Gabr at Camel Divers
Martin, Jo and the crew of *Ghazala Voyager*
Guido and crew of the *Coral Queen*
Kiki the frogfish girl

Special thanks to the contributing photographers listed below who have helped fill the gaps:
Didier Brandelet p.25br, p.59mr, p.73b, p.79tl, p.79ml, p.111tr, p.113mr; Helmut Debelius p.25tr, p.27tl, p.27tr, p.27bl, p.59bl, p.67ml, p.69tr, p.79bl, p.79br; Yolande Despres p.111bl, p.111br, p.113b; Itamar Grinberg p.35tr; Charles Hood p.27br, p.65tr, p.115tr;
F. Jack Jackson p.45mr, p.53br, p.67br, p.111ml1, p.111ml2; Frederic Pacorel p.79tr; Mark Webster p.23tr, p.39t, p.109bl, p.109br, p.111tl, p.111mr, p.113tl, p.113tr, p.113ml, p.115tl, p.115ml, p.115bl; Lawson Wood p. 33br, p. 37bl, p. 89ml.

Author's Acknowledgements

Jo and Morgan
Martin De Banks and Jo Farnham of *Ghazala Voyager*
Farag and Ali Sabri
Tony 'T-money' Nichols
Dr Goetz B. Reinicke, Deutsches Meeresmuseum (German Museum for Marine Research and Fisheries)
Dr Charles Sheppard, Department of Biological Sciences, University of Warwick
Jerry Kemp, Department of Biology, University of York

On behalf of the people of Sharm El Sheikh, this book is dedicated to Anton.

CONTENTS

FISHES

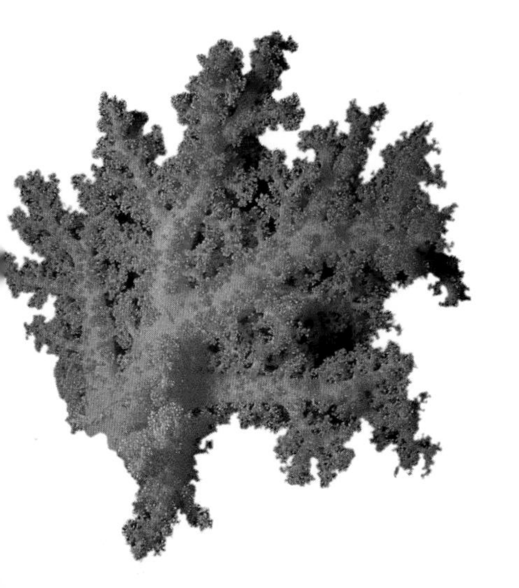

CORALS

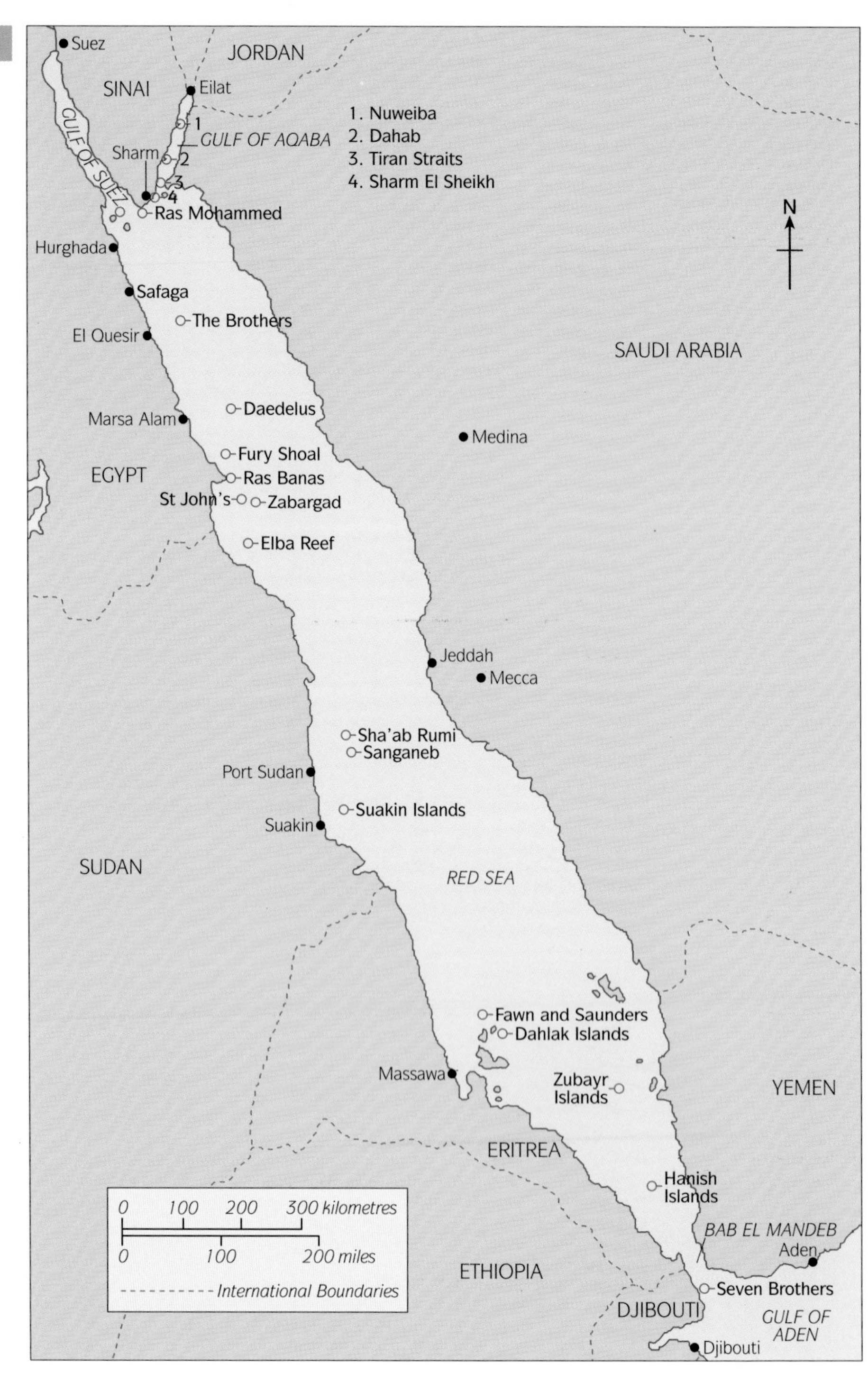

Suez
JORDAN
SINAI
Eilat
1. Nuweiba
2. Dahab
3. Tiran Straits
4. Sharm El Sheikh
GULF OF AQABA
GULF OF SUEZ
Sharm
Ras Mohammed
N
Hurghada
Safaga
The Brothers
El Quesir
SAUDI ARABIA
Daedelus
Marsa Alam
Medina
Fury Shoal
EGYPT
Ras Banas
St John's
Zabargad
Elba Reef
Jeddah
Mecca
Sha'ab Rumi
Sanganeb
Port Sudan
Suakin Islands
Suakin
SUDAN
RED SEA
Fawn and Saunders
Dahlak Islands
Massawa
Zubayr Islands
YEMEN
ERITREA
Hanish Islands
0 100 200 300 kilometres
0 100 200 miles
International Boundaries
BAB EL MANDEB
Aden
ETHIOPIA
Seven Brothers
DJIBOUTI
GULF OF ADEN
Djibouti

THE RED SEA

Stylophora pistillati surrounded by Glassfish, much to the annoyance of a pair of Red Sea Dascyllus.

For Europeans, the Red Sea is the closest tropical dive destination. One minute you're sitting on the airport runway, contemplating a grey winter sky, the next you're touching down on its rocky shores. A short flight can transport you from a world of nine-to-five keyboard-tapping and queuing on rain-sodden motorways, to a sea of swirling vortices of coloured fish. This is precisely why, over the last decade, the Red Sea has become such a popular dive destination.

The Red Sea is merely a sea-flooded rip in the earth's crust. It is a gaping vent, torn between the African and Arabian land masses. Down either side run chains of desert mountains, and looking at them you can almost see the power of continental plates tearing and buckling. Beneath the water's surface this scene continues in a dramatic seascape of valleys and canyons – a testament to the forces of volcanic activity that formed them.

Over 2,000km (1,250 miles) long, and in places up to 2.5km (1½ miles) deep, the Red Sea stretches from Israel and Jordan in the north, to Djibouti and Yemen in the south. Its unique ecology is the result of its geography. At its southern end the Red Sea is constricted by the narrow straits of Bab el Mandeb (The Gates of Sorrow), named for their ferocious storms. Here, not only does the Red Sea constrict, but it also runs shallow. This has effectively prevented the migration of species in and out of the Red Sea. For this reason, it is characterized by a huge number of 'endemic' species that are not seen elsewhere.

The greatest number of species are found in the south, affording the diver endless new sightings. In contrast, in the north, the colder water encourages large and uniform schools of fish, and this is perhaps the most impressive sight the Red Sea has to offer: huge swathes of anthias cloaking the reefs, great clouds of fusiliers. Each species lends its colour to the scene: coral pinks, fusilier blues, and anthias' gold against a backdrop of ultramarine.

Coral Reef Ecosystems

The role of coral reef ecosystems, like all of the earth's ecosystems, is to trap and circulate energy. The ultimate source of energy within this system is the sun, and it is the role of plants and corals to 'fix' this energy in a useful form: photosynthesis. This they do by using the sun's energy to fuel a reaction between carbon dioxide and water, combining the two to synthesize glucose, starch and eventually protein.

Although most corals are capable of photosynthesis, the main 'carbon fixers' are the benthic algae that cover the top of the reef. This zone is usually overlooked by divers, who rarely venture into such shallow water, but this is where the energy that drives the whole system is being harnessed.

The next level in the typical ecosystem contains the herbivores, and there are numerous species of reef fish that have specialized to fulfil this role. Parrotfish are the most obvious grazers, and they can be seen on every reef, gnawing away at the algae-clad surface. However, parrotfish are not the only species that fulfil this role: wrasses, surgeonfish, butterflyfish, rabbitfish, damselfish and many others use this handy food source.

Red-mouth Grouper, Lionfish and soft corals.

Next in the food-chain are predators: groupers, trevallies, scorpionfish, snappers and morays. There is a seemingly endless list of species queuing up to take a bite at the hapless herbivore. But even they are on another menu, that of the higher predators: the sharks.

This is the basic picture, but it is highly oversimplified. For in the waters that wash over the reefs another ecosystem is ticking over, fuelled at the bottom by the photosynthetic activity of phytoplankton. In turn, these are fed on by zooplankton, which again are snapped up by fusiliers and garden eels, or by filter-feeders such as mackerel, mantas and Whale Sharks, or they might not be eaten by fish at all: they may be devoured by the polyps of corals, which are the very substance upon which the entire ecosystem rests. There are many such examples, but it is sufficient to say that the ecosystem of the coral reef is immensely complex.

One of the main things to impress the first-time diver is the density of life on the coral reef. This abundance leads to intense competition between species, which are forced to specialize to the areas in which they have the greatest competitive advantage. This is known as their 'niche'. These niches are defined by various factors that affect the availability of food: the strength of the current; the exposure to waves; the availability of light. Since all these factors vary in different habitats, the distribution of each species within these habitats varies accordingly.

Once the novice diver has got over the sheer number of fish, the next task is to try to work out where each species fits within the ecosystem. Thankfully, this is an impossible task, for it is the endless surprises that are what keeps many of us diving.

Symbiosis

Symbiosis is important to all ecosystems, but none more so than that of the coral reef. Symbiosis occurs where the lives of two organisms become tied together and, in coral reefs, this occurs at the most basic level. Corals are essentially colonies of tiny polyps, which build a limestone skeleton around themselves. Over time, these colonies merge and grow, then die and become incorporated beneath the next layer of living reef.

The coral polyps feed much like anemones, by snaring plankton from the surrounding water. Like anemones, they also benefit from a symbiotic relationship with algal cells. These algae, known as zooxanthellae, are incorporated into the very flesh of coral polyps, where they receive protection but have access to sunlight. In return, the zooxanthellae provide the polyps with some of their products of photosynthesis. This symbiotic relationship has given corals the competitive edge to evolve and flourish, now occupying a significant percentage of the world's surface.

Symbiosis can be seen in many other forms on the coral reef, for example that of the Graceful Prawngoby, which shares its burrow with the Bulldozer Shrimp. The shrimp, which is almost blind, keeps the burrow in order, in return for having a constant lookout, whose movements it senses with its long antennae that constantly follow the fish.

Cleanerfish and Shark Suckers are involved in equally pure forms of symbiosis, in which both parties benefit: these are known as mutualisms. However, there are also symbioses that are uneven, with one party gaining much greater advantage than the other. One example is the relationship between anemonefish and anemones. The anemonefish gains protection from the anemone's stinging tentacles, to which it is somehow immune. In return, the fish chases off butterflyfish or other species that attack the anemone's tentacles. But the relationship is distinctly one-sided, the fish enjoying far greater benefits than its host.

The final form of symbiosis is parasitism. Marine creatures are the hosts of a wide range of parasites, from worms in their guts to barnacles in their throats. Few fish, however, are parasites themselves. The one notable exception is the Pearlfish, which has the dubious acclaim of living within the anuses of sea cucumbers.

Responsibility

With the increasing popularity of scuba diving, ever more pressure is being placed on coral reefs. Humans are naturally clumsy in the water, and without making a conscious effort to do otherwise, they often end up destroying the very reefs they go to see. Nowhere is this more evident than in parts of the Red Sea, where generations of ignorant diving have damaged the fragile ecology.

In Hurghada, many reefs bear the scars of anchor damage. However, things are improving and Hurghada has its own reef-protection committee, HEPCA, which installs mooring buoys and teaches environmental respect to the dive-boat skippers. Outside HEPCA's jurisdiction, anchors are still tearing up reefs, in most cases because divemasters are too lazy to tie a mooring. If skippers and divemasters will not take responsibility for conservation, then it is up to the client to make a stand where damage is being done.

Underwater, divers can reduce their impact simply by finning carefully and avoiding contact with the reef. One can steady oneself on a visibly dead coral but should avoid picking things up, and 'souvenirs' should not be taken.

Swell beating on the seaward edge of a reef.

However, diving does not need to have a solely negative impact. As more people become aware of the coral reef, more may help protect it from the many more serious threats, such as: dynamite and cyanide fishing; sewage and agricultural pollution; silting as a result of landfilling and coastal development; the cutting of blocks to provide building material; and chronic oil pollution. The list is apparently endless, but it is one that will hopefully shorten as diving introduces more witnesses to the underwater world.

Dangers of the Reef

The coral reef is a competitive environment, and all fish species have evolved methods of avoiding predation. Some species are simply fast or very elusive. Others are just too big to eat. But the vast majority carry some kind of spine or poisonous toxin to dissuade potential predators.

Although few species are actually aggressive towards divers, many can inflict painful or even fatal injuries in self defence. (This usually happens if a diver is being clumsy or just plain stupid.)

Toxins are a vital form of defence to soles, pufferfish, boxfish and many other species. The toxin is secreted through the skin of soles and it has been experimented with as a shark-repellent. Tetrodotoxin is the toxin produced by puffers, and it is fatal to humans if eaten. It is one of the five most potent toxins known to man. Nevertheless, puffers are a delicacy in the Far East, where specially trained 'fuju' chefs remove the ovaries and intestine in such a way as to avoid contaminating the flesh, which only has low levels of toxin from which it gains a spicy flavour. All the same, several people die each year as a result of clumsy preparation. Furthermore, seafarers on commercial vessels often die from eating species of puffer with which they are not familiar.

Toxins can also be injected by fish such as stingrays, stargazers, stonefish, scorpionfish and lionfish. In these cases it is usually the result of having stepped on the fish. The stingray has sharp feather-shaped quills in its tail, which is whipped forward to plant them in the unsuspecting swimmer's leg. Stonefish, scorpionfish and lionfish have stout dorsal fins, which are erected when threatened and can deeply puncture whoever steps on them. Lionfish stings are rarely fatal, but those of stonefish and scorpionfish can be. The affected limb should be submerged in very hot water (60–70°C/140–160°F), and held there for several hours. This has the effect of denaturing the protein-based toxin, much like hard-boiling an egg.

Electric defences have been evolved by both torpedo rays and by stargazers. A stargazer can deliver a very nasty shock, while that of the torpedo ray is usually mild. In fact, I once met a diver who tried to get a shock at every opportunity, just for kicks.

Schooling Black Snappers hang on the edge of a reef drop-off.

Sharp teeth are a characteristic of sharks, morays and barracudas, all of which are cursed with a bad reputation. Red Sea barracudas are not dangerous, and it is their Caribbean cousins that have earned the notoriety for them: many Caribbean divemasters perform macho stunts for their guests by hand or mouth-feeding barracudas. Obviously, now and then someone gets bitten and ironically it is the fish that gets the bad reputation.

Likewise, morays have a fearsome appearance. As a result, foolish divers occasionally think it cool to drag them from their holes and drape them round their necks. Understandably, the fish think otherwise. Given the long backward-pointing teeth, the bites can be severe, and although the fish is only protecting itself, it is branded a biter.

In contrast, some sharks do actually appear to want to eat humans. They are, however, in the minority. In the Red Sea, Oceanic Whitetips, Silkies, makos, Tigers, and Bull Sharks are the only potential man-eaters. Bull Sharks never venture far north of Djibouti and Tigers and makos are hardly ever seen.

This leaves Oceanics and Silkies, both of which should be treated with caution. They most frequently come into contact with divers at Egypt's offshore islands, for example Elphinstone and The Brothers. They are surface-dwelling species that scavenge turtles and sick dolphins. Given that dolphins are quite capable of hurting a shark, they approach potential prey with caution, nudging several times to test for a reaction before biting. This is your cue to leave the water.

A much greater concern to the average diver is triggerfish. The Titan Triggerfish is probably the Red Sea's most aggressive animal and in August and September when it is nesting, it viciously defends its brood. Its territory extends upwards from its nest, in an inverted cone that stops only at the surface. If attacked, divers should move away horizontally, keeping their fins between them and the demented fish.

Invertebrates too have a wide range of defences, the most serious being those of the conefish. This cone-shaped gastropod has evolved barbed teeth that can be hydraulically fired at passing fish. Usually, it lies hidden beneath the sand, waving its siphon in the water above. Any fish that mistakes this for a worm receives a poisoned barb in the mouth. The barb is attached to the cone by a fine thread, which holds the dying fish.

If the fish struggles it can damage the fragile conefish, or attract the unwelcome attention of predators. For this reason the gastropod has evolved an efficient toxin, more potent than that of the Black Mamba. Conotoxin is a highly effective cocktail of nerve poisons, which act at the nerve synapses to prevent electrical transfer. It also contains a heart-accelerator to ensure the venom is swiftly distributed around the body. Since humans have a similar nervous system to fish, we are prime victims.

According to anecdotal evidence, two casualties from conefish have occurred in the Red Sea. One involved a Textile Cone *Conus textile* that a diver wanted to take home as a souvenir. Having been told by the divemaster not to take shells, she concealed it inside her wetsuit, with obvious consequences. The other incident involved the Red Sea's other fatal species, the Geographic Cone *Conus geographicus*. A snorkeller had picked one from the seabed and was scraping the algae from its shell with a knife, when a barb entered the palm of his hand. He did not even make it as far as the shore.

Corals are also well armed. Fire corals and hydroids can both inflict irritating burns when touched, which can be treated with an acidic solution such as vinegar (or in desperation, urine). I once watched a diver break off a particularly beautiful frond of fire coral to take home as a souvenir. He then tucked it inside his wetsuit to conceal it from the divemaster and quickly realized his mistake. The sight of him struggling to remove the coral was hilarious, especially as in his frenzy he pushed it further down his long-john towards his groin. One can only wonder if he had vinegar at hand back on shore, or whether he had to rely on his friends for the alternative treatment.

This last anecdote illustrates how to avoid injury when diving in the Red Sea: don't touch and you won't get hurt. This long list of poisonous species may well sound off-putting, but if you learn to recognize them and exercise some common sense you'll be fine.

Classification

Classification may seem dull, but it is an important topic. It is essentially a filing system for all the world's organisms, and is used to catalogue the millions of species and their kinship to each other. Latin is used as the language of classification.

All organisms described in the first part of this book belong to the kingdom Animalia. That is to say they are not plants, nor are they fungi or microbes. Furthermore, they all have backbones, slotting them into the phylum Chordata and the subphylum Vertebrata. Here things start to diverge, at the level known as class.

At the current stage of evolution, fish fall into three classes: the bony fish (Osteichthys), which comprise the majority of species within this book, the cartilaginous fish (Chondrichthys), which are represented by the sharks and rays, and the lampreys and the hagfish (Agnatha), which are not represented here.

The Red Sea's Reefs

With respect to its corals, the Red Sea can be divided roughly in two, with the line provided by the Sudan–Eritrean border. To the south of this line, the reefs are generally rocky, with limited coral growth, while to the north they are generally steep coralline walls surrounded by deep blue water. But even within these zones, the variation is immense.

At its northern end the Red Sea is split into two: the Gulf of Suez, and the Gulf of Aqaba. The latter is a continuation of the Afro-Syrian rift system, a trench between continental plates that starts in the Rift Valleys of Central Africa. As such, its waters are deep, in places nearly 2km (1¼ miles) deep. It is also narrow: only 26km (16 miles) at its widest point, and less than 4km (2½ miles) where it joins the main Red Sea at the Tiran Straits.

Given its immense depth and narrowness, the Gulf of Aqaba's reefs are mostly steep walls. From Eilat as far as Ras Atantur, the sea is separated from the mountains by a coastal strip about 5km (3 miles) wide. There is a narrow fringing reef before the seabed descends, rising in places to form offshore shoals, then plunging again to over 1,000m (3,300ft).

From Ras Atantur to Nabeq, the mountains plunge almost directly into the sea, stopping only for the narrowest of fringing reefs, before plummeting to depths of 1,800m (5,900ft). Because of the extreme depth, sediment, once settled at the bottom, is never stirred back up. The result is clear water, despite strong northerly desert-winds and rough seas most of the year.

At the Tiran Straits, the gulf narrows and becomes shallower, forming a tight bottleneck. This causes a magnification of the tides flowing in and out of the gulf and the end result is ferocious currents. They are strongest two to three days after a full moon, and can run in excess of six knots in some places.

Down the middle of this strait, a huge ridge pushes up from the sea floor. On its four peaks coral reefs have formed: these are the reefs of Tiran. They are named, like many reefs of the Red Sea, after British admirals: Gordon, Thomas, Woodhouse and Jackson. The strong currents that sweep their slopes bring nutrients for the corals. The reefs are therefore extremely rich, and are characterized by walls of bright softcorals and gorgonians.

From Tiran to Ras Mohammed at the tip of the Sinai peninsula, the beaches are progressively replaced by raised fossil reefs. At Ras Mohammed itself, these take the form of high, soaring, limestone cliffs. Ras Mohammed's position, jutting out from the Sinai, dictates strong currents year round and like Tiran, this has resulted in especially luxuriant coral growth.

In contrast to Aqaba, the Gulf of Suez is a wide shallow basin, with average depths of 20–30m (65–100ft). The fringing reefs are less developed than in Aqaba and, instead, there is an intricate network of lagoons and barrier reefs, for example Sha'ab Mahmoud. Like Aqaba, the gulf is bordered on either side by high mountains. Hot desert winds from the north are channelled between these mountain ranges, leading to choppy seas most of the year. However, unlike Aqaba, the seabed is shallow and is easily stirred up. Combined with the effects of wind-blown desert sand, this results in turbid waters.

The Gulf of Suez has been the main east–west trade route since long before the Suez Canal was built. Its thousands of patchy reefs have caused the demise of many ships passing through, and their smashed hulks, heavily encrusted in sponges and corals, litter the reefs. To the south of the gulf are the resorts of Hurghada and Safaga. Both areas are characterized by wide bays with shallow patchy reefs. Bounding the outside of both bays are chains of steep reefs, which on their outermost sides plunge to considerable depths. The prevailing currents are from the north for most of the year, although there is usually a brief reversal around June.

The southern Egyptian coastline is typified by walls and drop-offs. Most of the diving, however, occurs on the offshore reefs and islands. The Brothers, Daedelus reef, Rocky island, Zabargad Island and Elphinstone are the most famous names. Nearer to the coast are wide shoals: St John's and Fury Shoal. Both are hugely diverse, with excellent diving.

Anthias feeding in the current on the reef wall.

This pattern is mirrored in Sudan, with the offshore reefs of Elba, Abingdon, Angarosh, Sha'ab Rumi and Sanganeb in the north, and the Suakin archipelago in the south. Here, species diversity reaches its maximum due to widely variable physical and biological parameters. It is off Port Sudan that the Red Sea has its widest (306km/190 miles) and deepest points (3,040m/9,9974ft).

The diving is much like the offshore reefs of Egypt, but the north–south distribution of species is reversed: while hammerheads and other sharks frequent the northern spurs of Egyptian reefs, it is on the southern plateaus of Sudan that they are most prolific. This is a reflection of a change in the prevailing winds and currents. From November to April, surface currents flow from the south and for the rest of the year they flow from the north.

Coastal Sudan is typified by narrow fringing reefs, while barrier reefs run parallel to the coast 2–5km (1–3 miles) offshore.

It was here that a macabre discovery was reported: the bleached bones of dozens of African pilgrims. Unscrupulous ferrymen offering the trip across the Red Sea to Mecca had pulled up on these remote beaches at night, claiming they were just off the Saudi coast. While the pilgrims slept, awaiting the sunrise to make the last stretch, the ferrymen would sneak off having already taken the money. They would return weeks later to search the bodies for valuables.

Heading south, Fawn and Saunders reefs are the last of the blue-water drop-offs. From here on, the reefs are typically rocky terraces, with slight coral encrustation.

Eritrea owns the western coast of the Red Sea, almost down to its southernmost end. In the south are numerous granite outcrops, such as Sayal Island and Harbi Island, but the most significant islands are those of the Dahlak archipelago. There are over 300 islands; the inner ones have little coral growth but the outer ones are slightly better. The larger islands are of limestone, which underwater is covered by a thin veneer of life, with Staghorn Coral and Fungiidae corals predominating.

Crossing to the eastern coast, one reaches the Zubayr and Hanish groups of Yemen (at the time of writing, a matter of dispute with Eritrea). In places, large limestone buttresses emerge from the sea, for example Quoin Rock or the Abu Ali islands. In others, there is little more than a jumble of granite blocks denoting the reef's presence.

It is often stormy and a southerly wind from Bab el Mandeb (The Gates of Sorrow) can persist for weeks. This is Whale Shark and Manta territory, but it is also home to a fascinating array of corals and sponges, which cling tenuously to the jagged slopes.

At the southernmost limit of the Red Sea is Djibouti and Bab el Mandeb. Much of the diving, for example the Isles de Mouche, is fairly uninspiring, but the Seven Brothers are arguably the Red Sea's best. Off limits until recently, the islands are positioned on the western side of the Bab el Mandeb shipping lane. Not only do the straits narrow here, but they also become shallower and, as with all straits, tidal movements are magnified. The strong currents that result are what feeds the region's remarkable fauna.

Most of the rock is volcanic and, on certain islands, for example Rhounda Dabali, coral growth has been completely stunted, presumably by minerals within the rock. Other islands, for example Horod le Rhale or Rhounda Khomaytou, have been thickly colonized. Large brain corals are common in the shallow water and black coral bushes encrust the deeper ledges.

When the tide is running, cold upwellings emerge from beneath. But while deep waters are generally clean in the Red Sea, those of Bab el Mandeb are dark and murky. It may not be good for divers, but Whale Sharks love it, and are often observed on the thermocline where this water mixes with the sparkling blue water above.

Corals

Reef-building (hermatypic) corals belong to the order Scleractinia, which itself is part of the phylum Cnidaria. As such, their closest relatives include jellyfish, hydras and anemones. Corals can therefore be thought of as colonies of hard-shelled anemone-like creatures. These are the coral polyps.

Coral polyps are not just superficially similar to anemones. Their anatomy is very similar too, with a tubular fleshy body, topped by tentacles. The tentacles are armed with stinging darts (nematocysts) that are used to paralyse prey, which is then seized and stuffed into the central mouth. Beneath the mouth, at the centre of the body is a stomach, which, like the anemone, has no anus.

The main prey is zooplankton, but in most species this is not enough. A second source of nutrition is gained from algal cells that live within the skin of the polyp. These algal cells, known as zooxanthellae, feed by photosynthesis, like any plant. However, not all the sugars synthesized are retained by the zooxanthellae, some are leaked to the host polyp, supplementing its main diet.

Assorted soft corals stretch for the light.

The polyps protect themselves by secreting a hard turret of calcium carbonate (limestone) around them, known as a corallite. The polyp can extend outside this corallite to feed and can then retract in times of danger, or when light and food levels are low. The corallite is ridged with septae, which form a framework around the many 'mesenteries' that radiate from the polyp's stomach. The role of the mesenteries is to increase the stomach's surface area, which aids absorption of nutrients.

The septae are key features in identification of different coral species, but they cannot be seen in a photograph. For this reason, only the genus name has been given for some photographs.

Corals reproduce both sexually and asexually. Asexual reproduction is by budding off from existing polyps. Sexual production is by the production of eggs and sperm, which fuse to form a free-swimming larva. This larva will then head off, to find a suitable patch on which to settle and form a new colony.

Soft coral and gorgonians adorn a cave wall.

Threats to Corals

Corals have very specific needs, and even the most minor changes in their environment can have severe effects. Factors such as temperature, turbidity, light levels and wave action all play key roles in a colony's success. Man's impact should also not be underestimated.

Since the Red Sea is surrounded by desert, it does not suffer many of the threats that face some of the world's reefs. Since there is virtually no river input, threats such as industrial and agricultural run-off are negligible. The desert is sparsely populated and therefore sewage pollution is also non-existent in most regions.

Nevertheless, where tourism is thriving, for example in Egypt, sewage is a factor. The problem with sewage is that it raises the water's nutrient level, encouraging algal growth, which eventually smothers the reef. Sewage from hotels is mostly treated and dealt with on land, making the input from boats the greatest threat. This is accentuated by the fact that dive-boats seek out healthy reefs to moor over. It is fortunate that most divers have the sense not to flush the boat toilets on site. But with the Egyptian Ministry of Tourism considering developing a major yacht cruising industry, things could get worse.

Another threat comes from construction. Around Hurghada, this is caused by landfilling: hotel owners buy coastal land, then expand it outwards, by dumping earth and rubble out into the sea. The result is that sediment enters the water, smothering corals downstream of the resort.

In Sharm El Sheikh, construction is more closely regulated. Nevertheless, there is a high windborne input of sediment into coastal waters. This is mainly sand and dust stirred up by construction vehicles, but inevitably it also includes harmful substances such as cement.

The Gulf of Suez harbours some of Egypt's greatest oil reserves. Although acute oil spills are thankfully rare, there is considerable damage from the chronic oil pollution. The beaches of some of the region's islands, for example, are heavily smothered in dried up oil. This is mirrored in some places beneath the water, with reefs showing signs of stress.

Cyanide fishing and dynamite fishing have not caught on in the Red Sea, as they have in other parts of Africa. In fact, fishing as a whole is fairly limited and does not pose the threat it does elsewhere. One exception is in Yemenese waters, where sharks are ruthlessly fished for their fins to sell to the Far East. In 1995, these fishermen came north and fished out the entire shark population of Sudan's Sha'ab Rumi. These 30 or so Grey Reef- and numerous Silver-tip Sharks had become accustomed to taking bait during the regular shark-feeds there, so they became an easy target.

Now, other sharks have moved in to replace them and Sudan has started patrolling its waters more vigorously. However, in Yemen, the problem remains: it is not uncommon to see beaches scattered with discarded shark bodies, fins and tails removed, the rest rotting in the sun.

There are also natural threats to reefs. The Crown of Thorns starfish *Acanthaster planci* is one well-known example. It feeds by extruding its stomach onto the coral to digest the living polyps, leaving behind a bleached skeleton. In some parts of the world, herds of these creatures have destroyed vast tracts of reef. Although the Crown of Thorns is present in the Red Sea, a healthy ecosystem appears to be holding it in check.

Elkhorn Coral is one of the more distinctive hard corals.

The Red Sea's 'fifteen-year storms' also have a devastating effect. Normally, in the northern Red Sea the prevailing winds come from the north. For this reason, delicate corals, such as *Acropora* species, grow on the sheltered south-facing reef slopes. Once in a while, however, huge swells are blown up from the south, crashing onto parts of the reef that are unaccustomed to heavy seas. The last one was in the winter of 1996, and it resulted in a lot of uprooted and broken table corals.

In addition, heavy rainfall over the mountains brought floods of mud and silt crashing through the wadis to pour into the sea. For weeks after, visibility was reduced to a few metres, but on this occasion the reef appeared to suffer no long-term damage.

Stressed corals are very susceptible to disease. Disease such as white band disease and black band disease advance along the coral colony, killing live tissue and leaving the empty skeleton behind. Black band disease is caused by the cyanophyte *Phormidium corallyticum*, while white band disease is caused by a bacterial pathogen, which is currently unidentified. Whatever the exact causes, it is well known that reefs stressed by pollution are far more susceptible to disease than those in healthy environments.

If this list of threats to corals is not enough, then there is also the impact of divers (*see* Responsibility p.7).

KEY TO SYMBOLS

This key describes the symbols that appear at the head of each species description. The symbols give a quick guide for the habit, diet and habitat of each species.

Habit

 single
 pairs
  groups
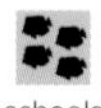 schools

Diet

plankton
fish
invertebrates
turtles
 mammals
 algae
 mixed corals

Habitat

 caves
 seagrass
  pelagic
sand
 reefs
 surface water

EXTERNAL FEATURES OF FISHES

This diagram illustrates the main structures of a fish referred to in the species descriptions.

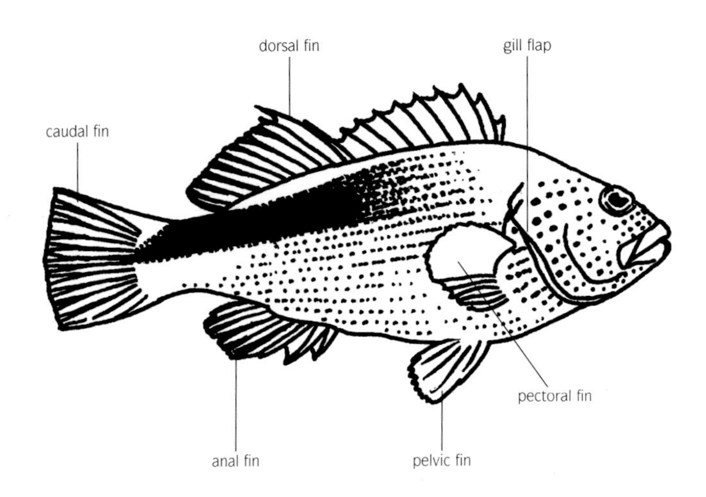

IDENTIFICATION GROUPS AND PICTORIAL GUIDE TO FAMILIES

Colour varies greatly between fish species, therefore it would seem an ideal means of identification. However, even within species, colour varies according to sex, age, region, season and surroundings. For this reason, body shape is a much more reliable means of identification. The following outlines represent all types of fish likely to be encountered in the Red Sea. Those sharing similar characteristics are grouped together for initial identification.

RAYS AND SHARKS

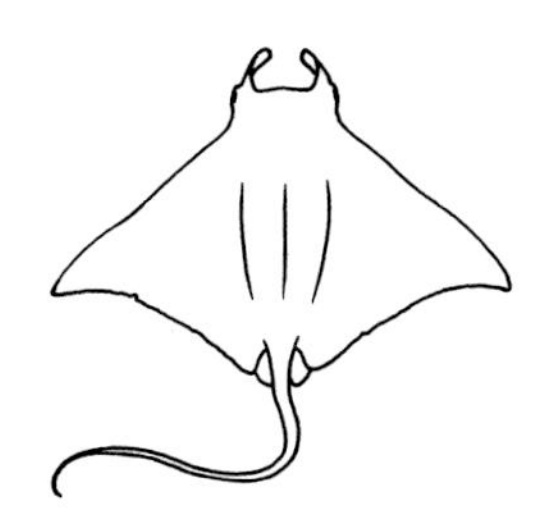

Mantas p.20

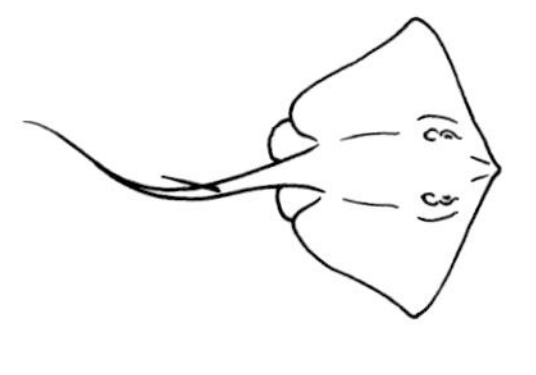

Stingrays pp.20–22

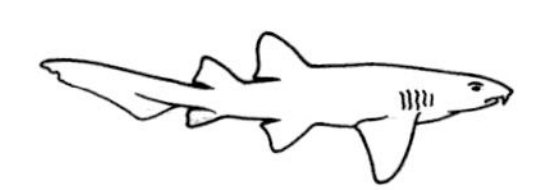

Reef sharks p.24

Carcharhinid sharks pp.24–26

Hammerheads p.28

SILVERY BLADE-SHAPED FISH

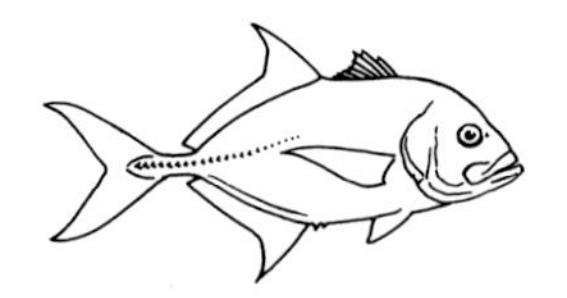

Trevallies pp.28–30

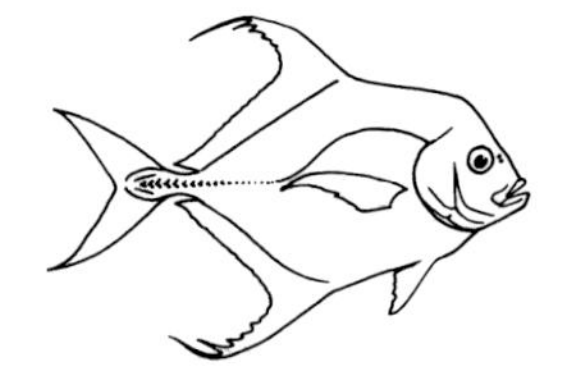

Pompanos p.32

SILVERY REGULAR-SHAPED FISH

Snapper p.40

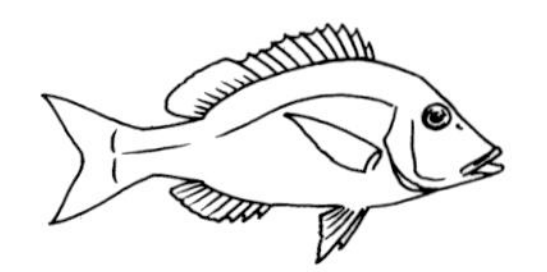

Emperor p.44

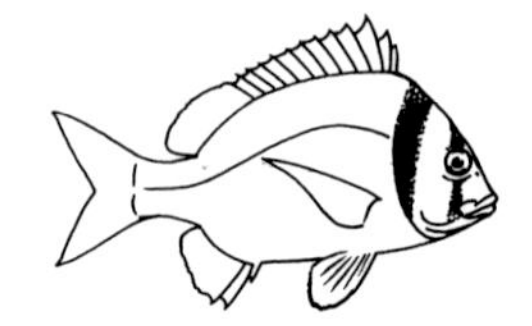

Bream p.44

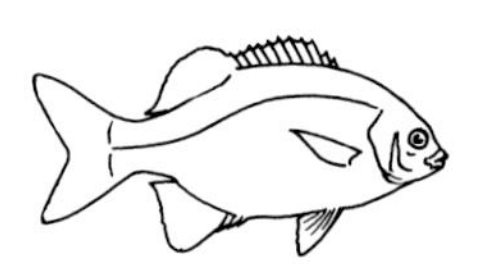

Rudderfish p.34

Sweetlips p.42

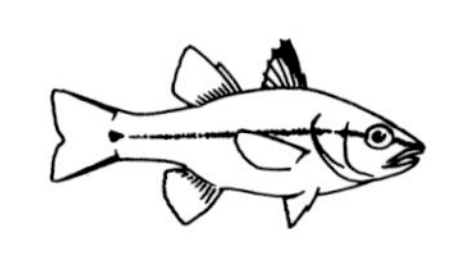

Cardinalfish pp.80–82

SILVERY TORPEDO-SHAPED FISH

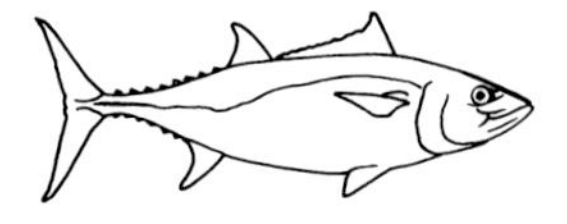

Tuna p.32

Mackerel p.32

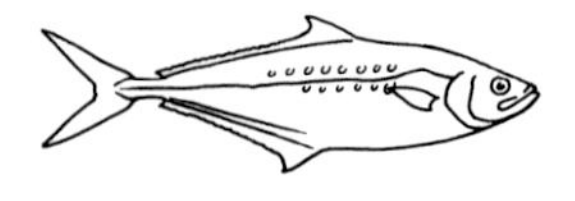

Queenfish p.32

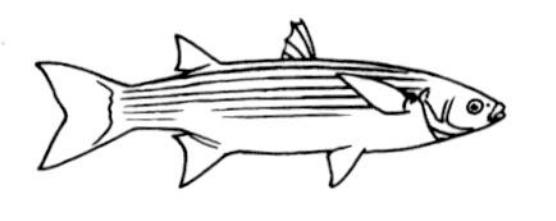

Mullet p.34

Milkfish p.34

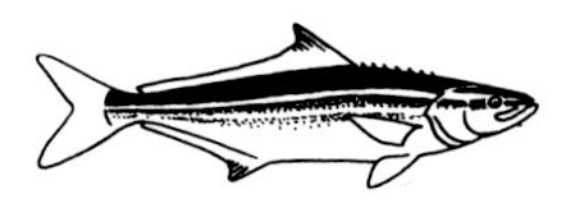

Cobia p.34

SILVERY ELONGATE FISH

Garfish p.34

Cornetfish p.36

Barracuda pp.36–38

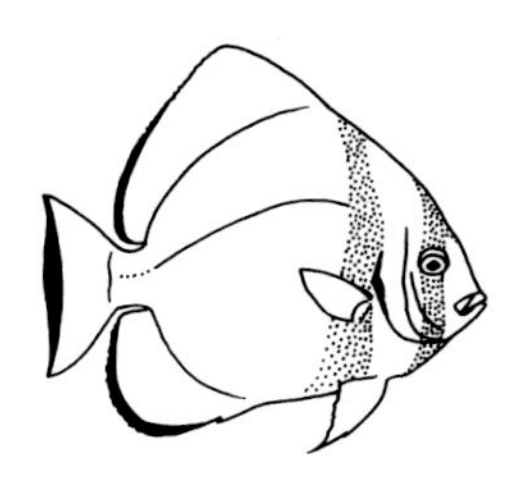

SILVERY IRREGULAR-SHAPED FISH

Spadefish p.42

ELONGATE BENTHIC FISH

Pipefish p.78

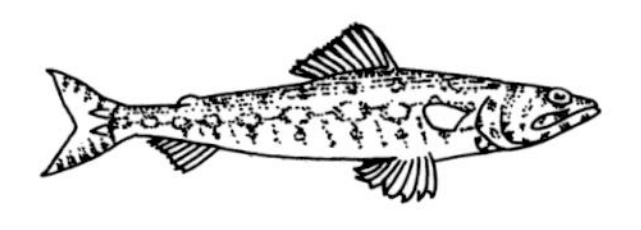

Lizardfish p.70

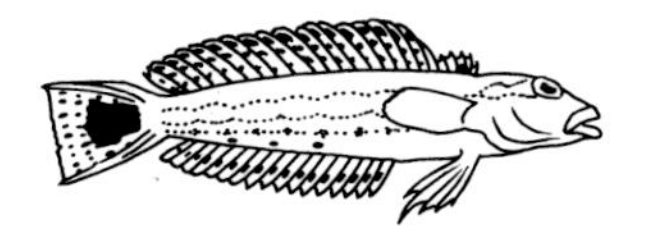

Sandperch p.70

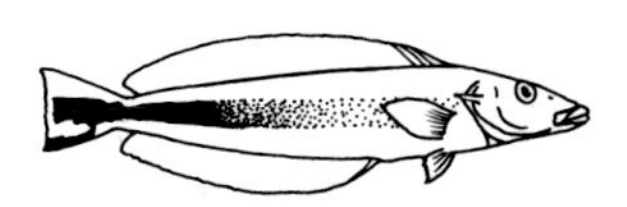

Tilefish pp.104–106

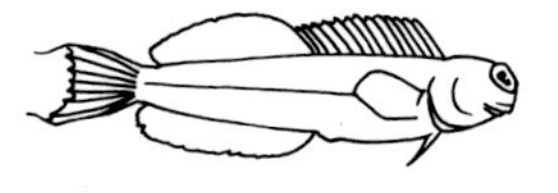

Blenny pp.108–112

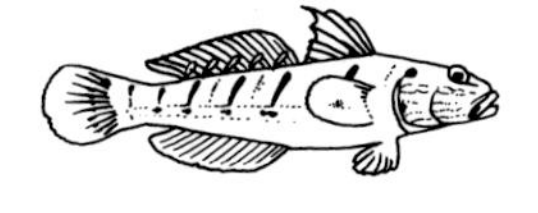

Goby pp.112–114

Moray pp.64–68

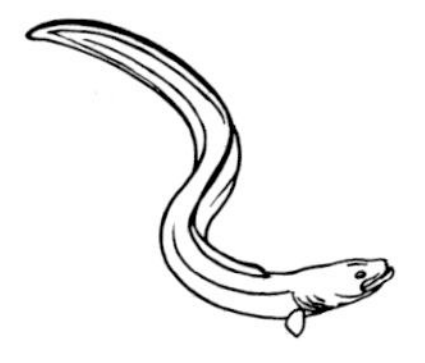

Conger p.68

IRREGULAR-SHAPED BENTHIC FISH

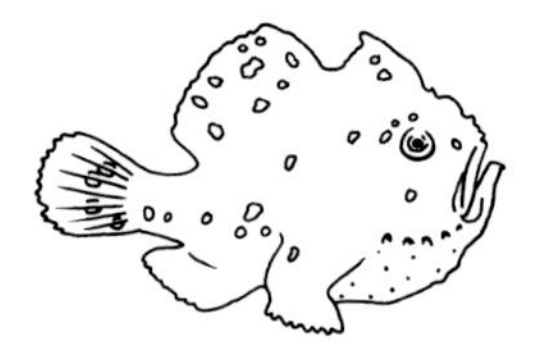
Frogfish p.76

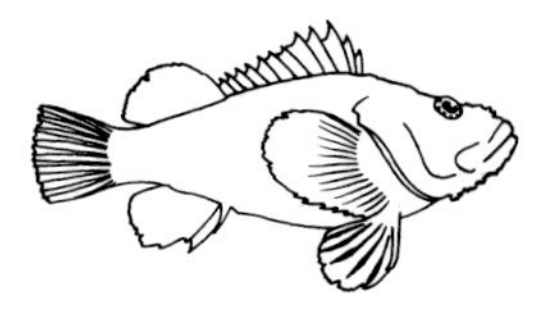
Scorpionfish p.72

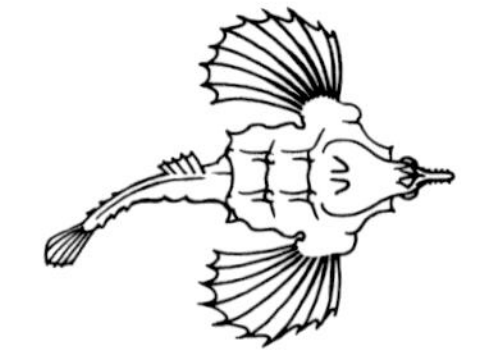
Seamoth p.74

Crocodilefish p.76

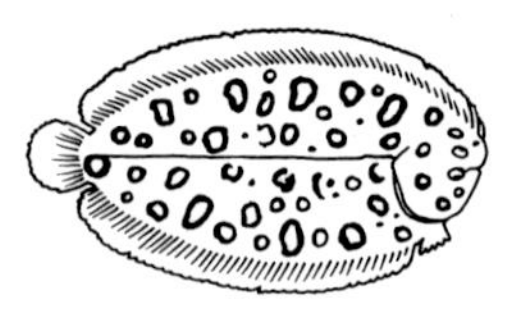
Moses Sole p.76

Lionfish p.74

Seahorse p.78

Ghost Pipefish p.78

REGULAR-SHAPED/SWIM WITH PECTORALS

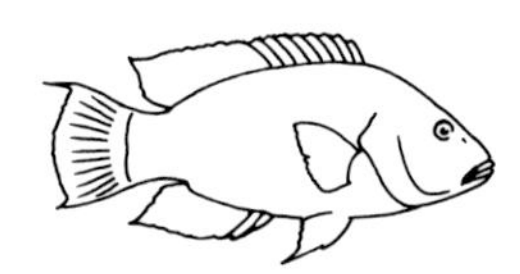
Wrasse pp.94–98

Hogfish p.100

Parrotfish pp.100–102

COLOURFUL REGULAR-SHAPED FISH

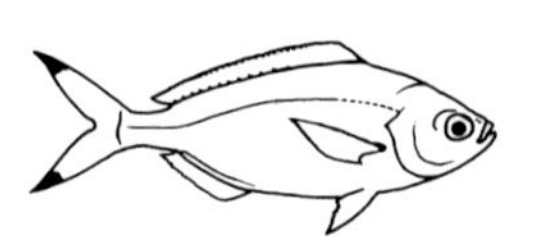
Fusilier p.38

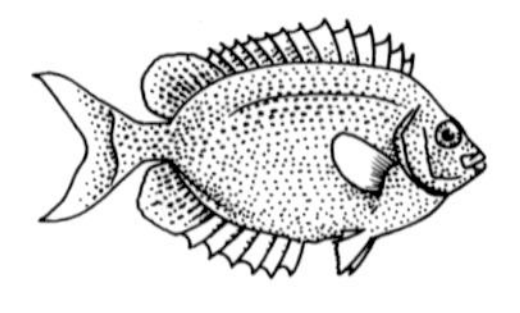
Rabbitfish p.48

Grouper pp.58–62

Hawkfish p.64

Goatfish p.104

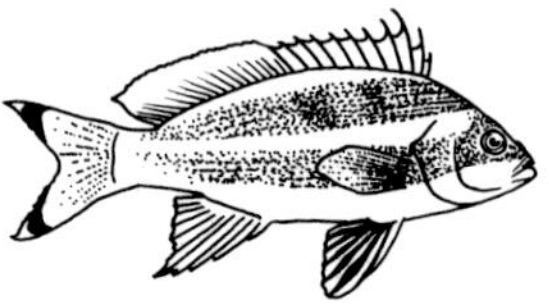
Fairy Basslet p.108

COLOURFUL IRREGULAR-SHAPED FISH

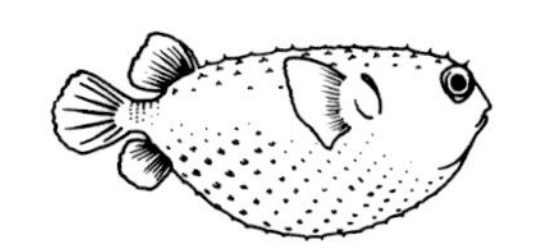

Porcupinefish p.56

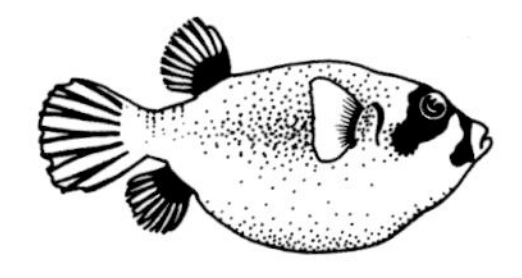

Pufferfish pp.56–58

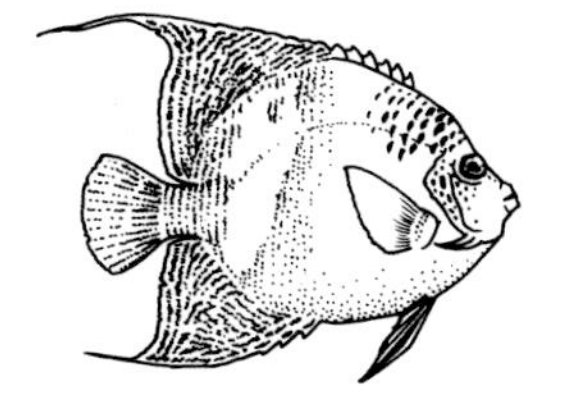

Angelfish pp.88–90

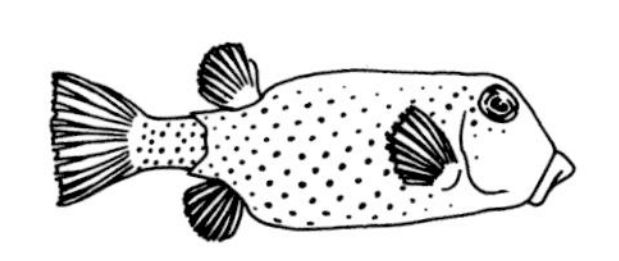

Boxfish p.54

Bannerfish p.94

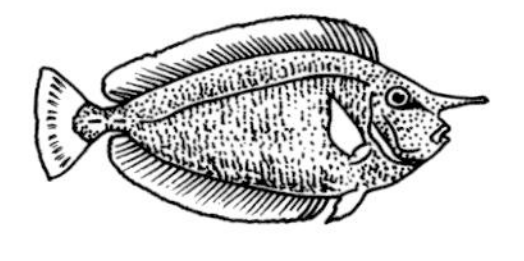

Unicornfish p.46

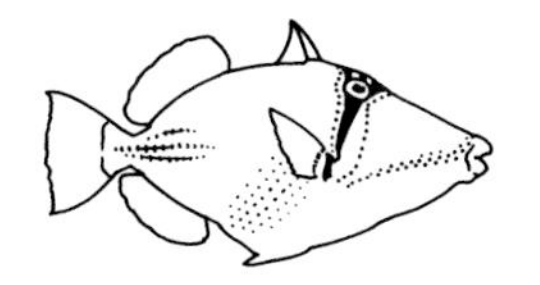

Triggerfish pp.50–52

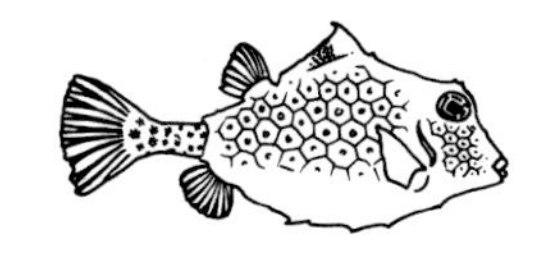

Turretfish p.54

COLOURFUL OVAL-SHAPED FISH

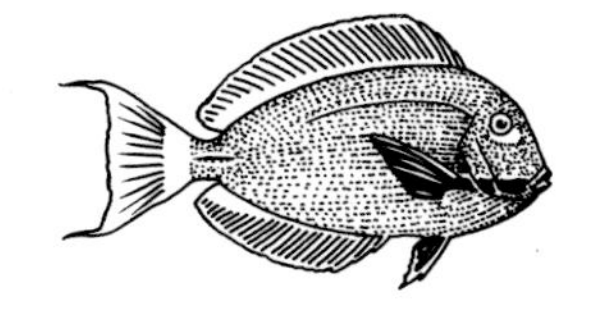

Surgeonfish pp.46–48

Butterflyfish pp.90–92

BIGEYED/CAVE-DWELLING FISH

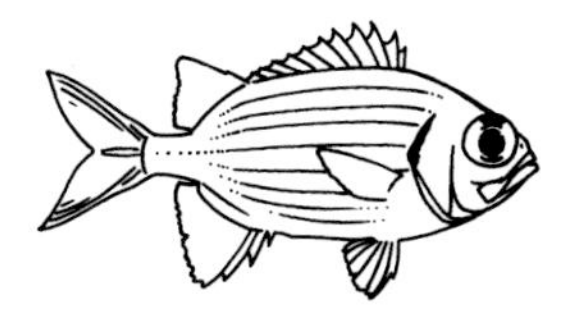

Soldierfish p.82

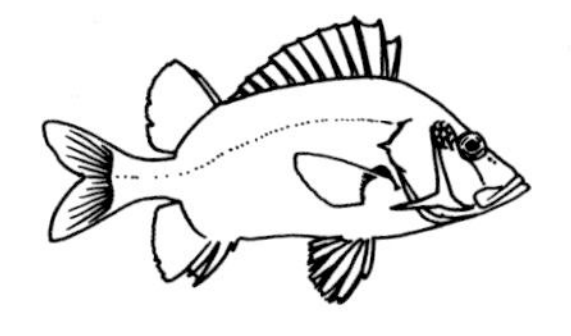

Squirrelfish pp.82–84

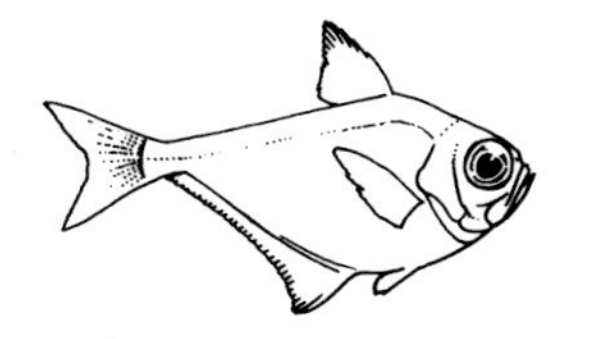

Hatchetfish p.80

Sweeper p.80

Bigeye p.82

RAYS AND SHARKS

Sharks and rays are cartilaginous fishes, in that they have no real bones. Instead, their skeleton is composed of cartilage, which lends them added flexibility and manoeuvrability. More importantly, they differ from bony fish by lacking a swimbladder. This means that the lift to prevent them from sinking must be generated through dynamic means. This lift is generated in two ways. First, the body and pectoral fins are shaped like aerofoils, and translate forward motion into upward lift in the same way as do the wings of a plane. Second, in the case of sharks the caudal fin has an elongated upper lobe, which lends additional downward thrust. Hence the myth that sharks sink if they stop swimming is essentially true.

Another major difference between sharks and bony fish is that sharks simply cannot stop. The reason for this is that where the fins are attached to the body they have a broad fixed base. So, whereas bony fish can swivel their pectoral fins to provide backward thrust, bringing themselves to an abrupt halt, sharks cannot. The nearest they come to stopping is performing an abrupt U-turn. This lack of slow, precise manoeuvrability probably explains why sharks have never evolved into herbivores and grazers.

The rays can be roughly divided into two groups: pelagic rays, such as mantas, and benthic species, such as stingrays. Pelagic rays feed by filtering plankton and small fish from the water column, whereas benthic rays feed by unearthing crustaceans and fishes from the seabed.

Sharks can be roughly grouped into bottom-dwelling species such as leopard and nurse sharks, or pelagic sharks, such as makos and threshers, although there is a degree of overlap. Divers have little to fear from sharks in the Red Sea. Although some species are potentially dangerous, there have been very few recorded attacks (*see* p.9).

1 MANTA

Manta birostris

 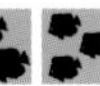  

Width up to 800cm (26ft). This large pelagic ray has distinct head-flaps on either side of its mouth. The ventral side is white and the dorsal side has shades of black and grey, sometimes with white markings. The gills are positioned ventrally. Its swimming motion is distinctive, with slow strokes of its wings, although it can put on an impressive burst of speed if the need arises. *Ecology:* It is seen singly or in small groups usually in channels and bays, and often at the surface. It feeds by filtering plankton and small fish from the water. Divers are occasionally visited on night dives by mantas, which feed on plankton attracted to the torches.

2 SPOTTED EAGLE RAY

Aetobatus narinari

Width up to 300cm (9ft 10in), but is typically less than 200cm (6ft 7in) wide. This ray is white ventrally and dorsally is chocolate brown with white spots or rings. It swims with graceful beats of its broad wings, but can turn on the speed when necessary. Unlike mantas, the head is distinct from the body. A small spine is located at the base of the extremely long tail. *Ecology:* This species is seen singly or in pairs in seagrass beds, sandy coral reefs and lagoons throughout the Red Sea. Here, it digs for crustaceans, molluscs, octopuses and fish.

3 FEATHERTAIL STINGRAY

Hypolophus sephen

Up to 180cm (6ft). This stingray is identified by its deep body and steep forehead. Its long tail has a broad feather of skin beneath it. *Ecology:* It is found throughout the Red Sea on shallow sandy reefs. It is particularly prevalent in the Gulf of Suez, at sites such as Stingray Station or Fossma Kebir, where it can be seen at night in large groups. It is usually seen lying on the seabed, covered in sand, rising and bolting when approached by divers. It feeds on benthic fish and invertebrates, which it digs from beneath the sediment.

1 Manta

2 Spotted Eagle Ray

3 Feathertail Stingray

4 LEOPARD WHIPRAY

Himantura undulata

Width up to 180cm (6ft). This elegant fast-swimming ray appears wider than it is long, and is almost identical in appearance to the Honeycomb Whip-ray *H. uarnak*. It differs, however, by having spots rather than rings patterning its dorsal surface. Its head is distinctly pointed, and its tail is very long and whip-like. *Ecology:* This species favours sandy reefs and lagoons and is found throughout the Red Sea. It feeds on fish and crustaceans. This picture was taken at Shark Reef, Ras Mohammed.

5 THORNY STINGRAY

Dasyatis sp.

Width up to 150cm (5ft). Like the Feathertail Stingray, this species has a deep body and a steep forehead. Unlike the Feathertail Stingray, however, it has a thorny ridge running down the centre of its back, and a thorny tail. It is generally dull grey in colour. *Ecology:* This species is usually seen in the central Red Sea, and only rarely is it found north of Sudan. It favours lagoons, where it can dig for shellfish beneath the sand.

6 ROUND RIBBONTAIL RAY

Taeniura melanospilus

Width up to 160cm (5ft 3in). This ray is round in shape, with soft flexible wings. The dorsal side is marbled grey in colour, with black spots. Ventrally it is white. The tail is laterally compressed, with wide lobes. It swims with a rippling undulation of its wings. *Ecology:* It is found through a wide depth range on coral reefs throughout the Red Sea. In particular, it favours mixed reefs and the sandy floors of caves. In these habitats, it feeds on sand-dwelling fish, shrimps and molluscs. This ray has frequently been seen at Thomas Reef in the Tiran Straits, while the photograph shown here was taken at El Quesir.

7 BLUE-SPOTTED RIBBONTAIL RAY

Taeniura lymma

Width up to 80cm (2ft 7in). This ray is relatively small and round in shape. The dorsal side is sandy in colour, punctuated with electric-blue spots. The sandy coloured tail is laterally compressed with wide lobes and is armed with two venomous spines. It swims with smooth undulations of its wings. *Ecology:* This is the most common of the rays and is found in sandy lagoons, seagrass beds and reefs throughout the Red Sea. Certain reefs are inundated with this fish, for example Yolande Reef at Ras Mohammed. It usually lies partly buried in sand or beneath corals and digs for worms, hermit crabs, shrimps and sand-dwelling fish.

8 SCALLOPED TORPEDO RAY

Torpedo panthera

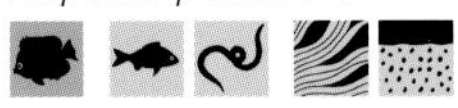

Width up to 80cm (2ft 7in). This small round ray is marbled and sandy in colour. Ventrally, it is white and it has a fleshy body with a short noticeably lobed tail. It swims with a distinctive wiggling motion of its body. If stepped on it can deliver a powerful shock. *Ecology:* It favours sandy seaward reefs, particularly in the northern Red Sea. Here, it feeds on molluscs, crustaceans and fish, which it stuns with an electric shock.

9 BOW-MOUTH GUITARFISH or ANGELSHARK

Rhina ancylostoma

Up to 300cm (9ft 10in). This fish has the chunky body and strong tail of a shark, with the wings of a ray. It is distinguished from other related species by its steep, horny-ridged back, heavy body and shark-like swimming motion. It is dark grey in colour, with dense white spots. *Ecology:* This bottom-dwelling species is quite rare in the Red Sea, favouring the sandy slopes beneath drop-offs, where it hunts out benthic fish and invertebrates. It is occasionally seen at Ras Mohammed's Shark Reef.

4 Leopard Whipray

5 Thorny Stingray

6 Round Ribbontail Ray

7 Blue-spotted Ribbontail Ray

8 Scalloped Torpedo Ray

9 Bow-mouth Guitarfish

10 WHALE SHARK
Rhincodon typus

Up to 18m (60ft) (but is typically 4–12m (13–39ft)), and 41,000kg (90,000lb) in weight. This is the largest living fish. It has white vertical bars alternating with white spots on a grey background. The body has a prominent lateral keel and long ridges on its dorsal sides. The mouth is wide and terminally positioned with small eyes on either side. A short barbel covers each nostril. *Ecology:* It is usually solitary and found in surface waters throughout the Red Sea, most notably in Djibouti and in Eilat. It is a pelagic species, but comes close to shore in regions of upwelling to feed on zooplankton, small crustaceans, fish and squid, which it filters through its gill arches.

11 TAWNY NURSE SHARK
Ginglymostoma ferrugineum

  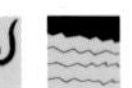

Up to 300cm (9ft 10in). Coloration ranges from grey to brown. The dorsal fin is set well back over the pelvic fins with a second dorsal fin just behind. The long tail almost lacks a lower caudal fin. Fleshy barbels border each nostril. Swimming is distinctive, with slow undulating sweeps of the long tail. It differs from a similar nurse shark, *G. brevicaudatum*, in tail length. *Ecology:* It is found on rugged seaward reefs and shallow lagoons predominantly in the southern Red Sea. Generally, it sleeps in crevices and beneath boulders by day, emerging at night to feed on fish, urchins, cephalopods and crustaceans, which are sucked from their hiding places.

12 WHITE-TIP REEF SHARK
Triaenodon obesus

   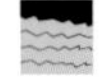

Up to 220cm (7ft 3in), but is typically less. This slender, tawny-grey coloured shark has a squarish head, prominent nasal flaps and distinct ridges over each eye. It is also recognized by the white tips on the tail fin and both dorsal fins. It swims with a characteristic wiggling motion. *Ecology:* It is often seen singly or in small groups, resting face into the current on sand patches. It is common on seaward reefs, lagoons and reef-tops throughout the Red Sea. It feeds at night, mainly on fish and octopus, which it pulls from crevices. The left photograph shows a White-tip in its typical environment, scavenging along the reef. The right one shows a much rarer sight of White-tips crammed tightly into a cave, in this case at Tiran island at the mouth of the Gulf of Aqaba.

13 LEOPARD SHARK, VARIEGATED NURSE SHARK or ZEBRA SHARK
Stegostoma fasciatum

   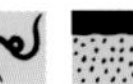

Up to 360cm (11ft 10in). This beautiful creature is sandy in colour, patterned with dark rings and spots. It has small barbels on its snout, and a tiny mouth and eyes. The two dorsal fins are positioned well back along its ridged body. It swims sluggishly with undulating sweeps of its very long tail. *Ecology:* It is usually found singly, resting on sand patches of channels and seaward reefs. It feeds by night on crustaceans, cephalopods, fishes and shellfish.

14 GREY REEF SHARK or LONGNOSE BLACKTAIL SHARK
Carcharhinus amblyrhynchos

Up to 230cm (7ft 7in). The body is grey with a white underside. The trailing edge of the tail has an indistinct black band. The dorsal fin is occasionally edged with white. This small powerful shark is more agile and graceful than the other reef-sharks. *Ecology:* It is often seen in packs on deep seaward reefs and drop-offs, especially in areas of strong current. It is an inquisitive shark that feeds mainly on fish, and is usually the first to appear at shark feeds, as shown here.

10 Whale Shark

11 Tawny Nurse Shark

12 White-tip Reef Shark

12 White-tip Reef Shark

13 Leopard Shark

14 Grey Reef Shark

15 SILVER-TIP SHARK
Carcharhinus albimarginatus

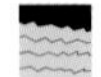

Up to 300cm (9ft 10in). This impressive creature is similar in shape to the Grey Reef Shark, though generally larger and stockier. It is Identified by the white trailing edges on all fins. The second dorsal fin is less than half the height of the first, and the pectoral fins are pointed. *Ecology:* It is a solitary fish, usually found deep on seaward reefs, offshore islands, shoals, walls and drop-offs. It is especially frequent in southern Egypt and Sudan. It feeds on a wide variety of fish, rays and small sharks, and is the dominant fish at shark feeds, chasing away Grey Reef Sharks, and only making way for serious predators such as Makos.

16 OCEANIC WHITE-TIP SHARK
Carcharhinus longimanus

Up to 350cm (11ft 6in). This pelagic species should be treated with great respect. It is tawny in colour with a white belly and mottled white tips to all of its large rounded fins (juveniles have black markings). Its huge pectoral fins are its most striking feature. *Ecology:* It patrols surface waters of the open ocean or offshore islands throughout the Red Sea. It feeds singly or in pairs on pelagic fish, squid, turtles, baitfish, seabirds, garbage and whale or dolphin carcasses. It has on occasions been seen following in packs behind pods of dolphins.

17 OCEANIC BLACK-TIP SHARK
Carcharhinus limbatus

Up to 250cm (8ft 2in). This stocky grey brown shark has a white underbelly, white anal fin and a pale slash on each flank. All other fins are tipped with black, particularly the undersides of the pectorals. Its powerful build distinguishes it from other similar sharks. The snout is pointed, with its back rising steeply up to the dorsal fin. It is a fast and capable predator. *Ecology:* It occurs singly or in small groups in shallows and inshore waters. Often seen at Ras Mohammed during the summer months. It feeds on schooling fishes.

18 SILKY SHARK
Carcharhinus falciformis

Up to 300cm (9ft 10in). This shark is named after the distinct sheen of its tawny brown body. It is similar in habits to the Oceanic White-tip Shark and should likewise be respected. Pectoral fins are long, narrow and pointed. The snout is sharp. It is identified by the second dorsal and anal fins which are wider than they are tall and have elongated trailing tips. *Ecology:* It is pelagic or semi-pelagic, favouring the surface waters. It often forms small hunting packs and feeds on baitfish, larger schooling fish and pelagic invertebrates. It has been known to harass divers (I have been bullied at night by a Silky, which was attracted to my torch beam).

19 SAND-BAR SHARK
Carcharhinus plumbeus

Up to 250cm (8ft 2in). This shark is grey with a white underbelly. It is immediately recognizable by the rounded snout, steep back and huge dorsal fin (over one-tenth the body length). *Ecology:* It often forms schools, sometimes mixing with Silky sharks, and has been seen at Ras Mohammed, mixing with the Silkies and Oceanic Black-tips there. It feeds mainly on bottom living fish such as eels, flatfish, rays or smaller sharks.

20 SHORT-FINNED MAKO SHARK
Isurus oxyrinchus

Up to 380cm (12ft 6in), but is typically less. This notorious relative of the Great White is capable of astonishing bursts of speed. Its body is deep indigo blue, fading to pure white beneath. It is characterized by a conical snout and very long gill slits. *Ecology:* This pelagic shark may come inshore, but only where there is deep water. Its fearsome reputation results from the spirited fight it puts up when hooked by game fishermen, among whom it is a popular fish. It has been reported at shark feeds, where it takes a dominant position over all other shark species. It feeds on tuna, mackerel, sailfish and other fast swimmers.

15 Silver-tip Shark

16 Oceanic White-tip Shark

17 Oceanic Black-tip Shark

18 Silky Shark

19 Sand-bar Shark

20 Short-finned Mako Shark

21 SCALLOPED HAMMERHEAD
Sphyrna lewini

Up to 330cm (10ft 10in). The hammerheads are identified by their broad flat hammer-shaped heads (known as a cephalofoil). The Scalloped Hammerhead is recognized from other family members by a curved front edge to its head. This edge is, as the name suggests, scalloped or lobed. *Ecology:* It is usually seen schooling around the thermocline on offshore reefs, for example the Egyptian reefs of Jackson, Elphinstone and Daedelus. It feeds on schooling fish, skates, rays and cephalopods.

The Great Hammerhead *S. mokarran* is generally larger, attaining a length of about 550cm (18ft), but it is typically about 400cm (13ft). The Great Hammerhead is distinguished from other members of the family by the almost straight, flat leading edge to its head. Its dorsal fin is characteristically tall with a curved rear margin. The base of the anal fin is wider than that of the second dorsal. Coloration is grey and white. It feeds primarily on skates and rays, but also takes other sharks and reef fish. It is a solitary species, and is very rarely seen in the Red Sea.

TREVALLIES, MACKEREL AND TUNA

Carangidae and *Scombridae*

Trevallies, or jacks as they are also known, are silvery fish with laterally compressed blade-like bodies. Their tails come to a narrow caudal peduncle, which is reinforced with bony scutes, and behind that the powerful tail is deeply forked. This genus favours areas of strong current, where their power lends them a competitive advantage. They are fast swimmers, often hunting in packs along reef walls, and can often be seen making a rush at the reef to snatch away small anthias or Glassfish. They are inquisitive fish, and the Orange-spotted and Giant Trevallies will come very close to inspect approaching divers.

Mackerels and tuna have more torpedo-shaped bodies than the trevallies, but they share the same silvery coloration and powerful forked tail. Some, such as the Spanish Mackerel, are solitary hunters along reef drop-offs. Others, such as the Dog-tooth Tuna form small hunting parties

1 GIANT TREVALLY
Caranx ignobilis

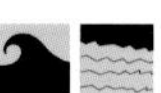

Up to 175cm (5ft 9in). The Giant Trevally is distinguished by its steep head profile and deep body. Coloration ranges from pale grey to gunmetal and the flanks are often scarred. *Ecology:* It is an aggressive predator, hunting singly or in packs, usually in areas of strong current, where it targets small schooling fish. Juveniles favour lagoons and estuaries, whereas adults prefer seaward reefs. It is an inquisitive species, often swimming aggressively up to divers and circling them.

2 BIG-EYE TREVALLY
Caranx sexfasciatus

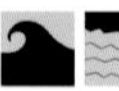

Up to 85cm (2ft 9in). This striking silvery fish is recognized by its large eyes and white-tipped second dorsal fin. *Ecology:* It is usually found along seaward walls and drop-offs, forming large schools, which split and encircle the approaching diver. It feeds aggressively on small reef fish and crustaceans. It is widely distributed throughout the Red Sea, but forms the largest schools in Egypt and Sudan.

21 Scalloped Hammerhead

21 Scalloped Hammerhead

1 Giant Trevally

2 Big-eye Trevally

3 BLUE-FIN TREVALLY
Caranx melampygus

Up to 100cm (3ft 3in). Blue dorsal and ventral fins identify this powerful fish, along with silvery-green pigmentation and black spots. *Ecology:* It is usually seen marauding in small packs along seaward reef walls, where it snatches reef fish and crustaceans. It is also commonly found near wrecks and caves, where it hunts for Glassfish that have strayed from the cover of darkness. It is much more prolific in the north than in the south.

4 THREAD-FIN TREVALLY
Alectes ciliaris

Up to 110cm (3ft 7in). This ghostly-pale fish has large dark eyes and unmistakable streamers on the anal and dorsal fins. *Ecology:* This bizarre creature is found only rarely in the Red Sea, Ras Mohammed being one location. Juveniles congregate in the surface layers of open water, where they mimic the jellyfish among which they drift. The adults are also usually seen in the surface waters, where they hunt.

5 YELLOW-SPOTTED TREVALLY
Carangoides fulvoguttatus

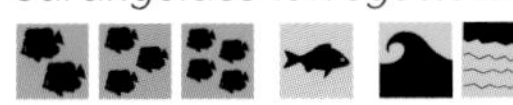

Up to 95cm (3ft 1in). Three black spots follow the lateral line in adults, and the silver flanks are coloured with yellow spots arranged into four vertical bands. *Ecology:* This species patrols in schools along seaward shore reefs and offshore seamounts, often in large schools. It feeds on small reef fish, which are hunted down with uncommon speed. It is widespread along the length of the Red Sea.

6 BLUE-BAR TREVALLY
Carangoides ferdau

Up to 70cm (2ft 4in). The silver body is marked with broad dark bands. In large adults the tail may develop a yellow tinge. *Ecology:* This species is usually seen schooling on sandy sheltered reefs, where it feeds on sand-dwelling shrimps and crabs. Adults often move singly in open water. In the summer, a large school can sometimes be found quite literally filling the shallow lagoon behind Shark and Yolande reefs at Ras Mohammed, where this picture was taken.

7 ORANGE-SPOTTED TREVALLY
Carangoides bajad

Up to 55cm (1ft 10in). Bold orange spots are usually arranged on a silver ground colour, although this small jack frequently turns completely yellow. *Ecology:* It usually forms large marauding schools, which hunt close to the reef. It is often seen worrying schools of Glassfish or diving at anthias hovering above the reef. It can sometimes be found opportunistically following packs of Yellow-saddle Goatfish, snatching up small fish flushed from cover.

8 GOLDEN TREVALLY
Carangoides speciosus

Up to 110cm (3ft 7in). This handsome fish has a deep muscular body. Coloration is pale silver, with gold tinges around the belly and ventral fins. The lips are large and rubbery, like a sweetlips. *Ecology:* This uncommon fish is mostly found in the southern Red Sea. It feeds on crustaceans, which it unearths from the seabed, as shown in the picture. Juveniles are reported to inhabit the tentacles of jellyfish, and small individuals act as pilots for sharks, dugongs and rays.

9 PILOT JACK
Naucrates ductor

Up to 70cm (2ft 4in). This small fast fish is unmistakable, with its bold black and silver stripes, and shark in tow. Unlike other trevallies, it has a fleshy keel to its tail instead of scutes. *Ecology:* It lives in groups or singly, accompanying pelagic sharks, with which it forms a commensal relationship. Oceanic White-tip Sharks are rarely seen in the Red Sea without at least half a dozen of these fish tagging alongside.

3 Blue-fin Trevally

4 Thread-fin Trevally

5 Yellow-spotted Trevally

6 Blue-bar Trevally

7 Orange-spotted Trevally

8 Golden Trevally

9 Pilot Jack

10 ALMACO JACK
Seriola rivoliana

Up to 110cm (3ft 7in). This species is silvery with a bold black stripe crossing diagonally over each eye. The pelvic fins are pronounced, with a pale leading edge. The second dorsal fin is also pronounced. *Ecology:* This lively fish is usually only seen by divers who enter into blue water. It is often seen following schools of Rainbow Runners, or in the company of sharks.

11 SILVER POMPANO
Trachinotus blochii

Up to 110cm (3ft 7in). This species has a deep, oval, silver body, and gold fins tinged with black. *Ecology:* Adults move in small packs, and feed on molluscs and shellfish from beneath the sand. Juveniles favour sandy lagoons, harbours and estuaries. This species is generally found on shallow reefs with strong current, for example Stingray Station in Egypt, or Ship Rock in the Yemen.

12 TWIN-SPOTTED QUEENFISH or LEATHERBACK
Scomberoides lysan

Up to 75cm (2ft 6in). This sleek torpedo-shaped fish has a faint line of black spots on either side of its lateral line. *Ecology:* Adults are often seen cruising along drop-offs or through open water. Juveniles favour shallow inshore waters and reef-tops.

13 RAINBOW RUNNER
Elegatis bipinnulata

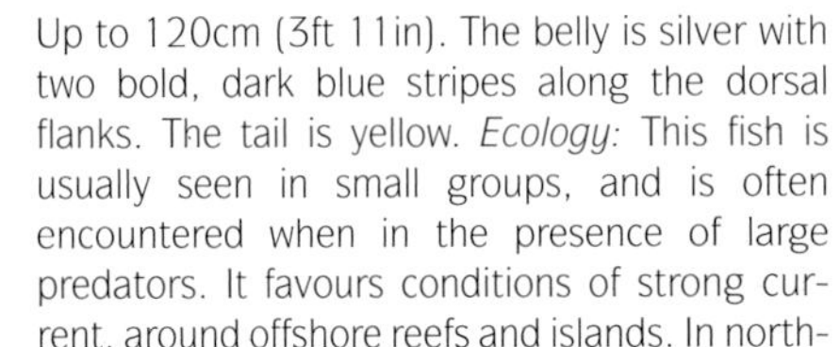

Up to 120cm (3ft 11in). The belly is silver with two bold, dark blue stripes along the dorsal flanks. The tail is yellow. *Ecology:* This fish is usually seen in small groups, and is often encountered when in the presence of large predators. It favours conditions of strong current, around offshore reefs and islands. In northern Egypt, it is usually seen in the summer on the current-strafed corner of Jackson Reef. In Sudan, it can be seen on the southern plateaus of most offshore islands.

14 SPANISH MACKEREL
Scomberomorus commerson

Up to 240cm (7ft 10in). The body is sleek, powerful and torpedo-shaped, and the head is comparatively long. The colour is silver with faint dark vertical bands. *Ecology:* This solitary semi-pelagic species is often seen hunting along reef walls and drop-offs. It feeds by isolating small fish from their schools, using its speed and manoeuvrability to close the gap.

15 DOG-TOOTH TUNA
Gymnosarda unicolor

Up to 200cm (6ft 7in). The flanks are deep blue or indigo, merging with a silvery belly. The body is thick and muscular, narrowing to a scaly caudal peduncle and a deeply forked tail. The lateral line is very prominent in this species. *Ecology:* The Dog-tooth Tuna is either solitary or forms small groups. It is usually seen cruising through mid-water, especially in areas where there is a strong current, where it voraciously hunts small jacks and fusiliers. Groups often have a home range, but these are best unmentioned to protect them from sport fishermen.

16 BIG-MOUTH MACKEREL
Rastrelliger kanagurta

Up to 40cm (1ft 4in). The body is silvery with striped dorsal flanks. The tail is deeply forked, and the caudal peduncle is narrow and scaly. *Ecology:* This species forms staggeringly large schools, which arrive in Egypt from the south in early summer. It feeds by scooping in water through the gaping wide mouth and filtering out the plankton with its gill rakers. Abu Kafan and Sha'ab Sheer in Safaga both attract sizeable schools in May and June.

10 Almaco Jack

11 Silver Pompano

12 Twin-spotted Queenfish

13 Rainbow Runner

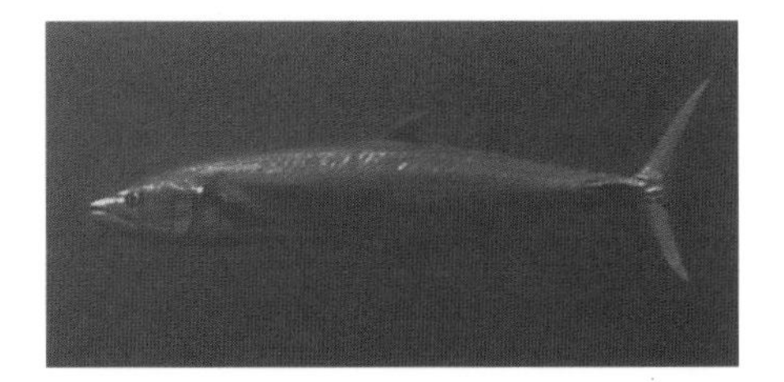

14 Spanish Mackerel

15 Dog-tooth Tuna

16 Big-mouth Mackerel

OTHER SILVERY FISH

A number of species fall outside the main family groupings. For convenience they have been grouped into two sections: this one and another entitled 'Other Reef Fish', which occurs later in the book. The species in this section live either in the surface waters or on sandy bottoms where their silvery coloration lends a degree of camouflage.

1 GARFISH

Tylosurus crocodilus

Up to 150cm (4ft 11in). The long cylindrical body gives way to a slightly broader head and a vicious bill armed with long teeth. It is uniformly silver in colour. *Ecology:* This species is a popular foodfish to the Bedouins, who name it 'Huhrman'. It is a solitary predator of shallow open water, and can often be seen patrolling along the edges of walls. It feeds on small fish, which it snatches with its long bill.

2 COBIA

Rachycentrum canadum

   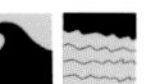

Up to 200cm (6ft 7in). The body is dark with a pale underside. The back is steep, and the overall profile is somewhat shark-like. The juveniles display a lateral white stripe, and are remora-like in appearance. *Ecology:* The Cobia accompanies large mantas, Honeycomb Rays and Eagle Rays. Less commonly, it is seen with sharks and turtles. As such, it can spend long periods offshore, living pelagically and sharing from its host's prey. Equally, those that accompany rays can be seen on coastal reefs waiting as the ray rummages in the sand.

3 MILKFISH

Chanos chanos

Up to 180cm (6ft). The long torpedo-shaped body is silver. The tail is dark and dramatically forked. The eyes are large, and the mouth is wide and terminally positioned. *Ecology:* It usually moves in small groups, feeding on benthic algae, or algae at the water's surface. When patrolling the surface, its large protruding fins are slightly shark-like, fooling many a naive observer. Hence, in Egypt, it has earned the name 'tourist shark'.

4 HIGHFIN RUDDERFISH

Kyphosus cinerascens

   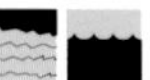

Up to 45cm (1ft 6in). Rudderfish are medium-sized, with small heads and small terminal mouths. This species is dark grey, and is identified from *K. vaigensis* by the high dorsal and anal fins. The chin is also slightly undercut, with a weak jaw-line. *Ecology:* The shallow surgy waters on seaward reefs often support small shoals of this species, often mixed with other species such as Black Snappers. It feeds on benthic algae, grazed from the reef-top.

5 LOWFIN RUDDERFISH

Kyphosus vaigensis

  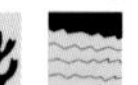

Up to 60cm (2ft). This is a silvery grey species with an ovaloid body and a tiny head. It is distinguished from *K. cinerascens* by the small dorsal and anal fins. The face also bears a dark downturned 'moustache'. *Ecology:* Whereas *K. cinerascens* prefers shallow surgy waters, this species prefers sheltered shady waters, such as those beneath jetties. Here, it feeds on algae growing on the jetty legs or on the shingle beneath. This picture was taken beneath a jetty in southern Egypt.

6 FRINGELIP MULLET

Crenimugil crenilabis

Up to 60cm (2ft). The mullets are silvery cylindrical fish. The snout is short, and the mouth is small with tiny teeth. The two dorsal fins are widely spaced. This species is identified from the two other Red Sea mullets, *Oedalechilus labiosus* and *Valamugil seheli*, by its wide upper lip with prominent papillae, and by the faint spot on the base of the pectoral fin. *Ecology:* It occurs singly or in small shoals roving across shallow sand patches and lagoons, grazing on algae and detritus.

1 Garfish

2 Cobia

3 Milkfish

4 Highfin Rudderfish

5 Lowfin Rudderfish

6 Fringelip Mullet

7 BARRED FLAGTAIL

Kuhlia mugil

Up to 20cm (8in). The family *Kuhliidae* are small, laterally compressed fish with deeply notched dorsal fins. at first sight, this species is fusilier-like in appearance, but the black and white barred tail and silvery coloration soon give it away. *Ecology:* The adults form dense schools in shallow surgy water along exposed shorelines. They are infrequent in the Red Sea, with one notable school occurring just off the jetty at Big Brother Island. The juveniles inhabit tidepools and surge channels. The schools disperse at night to feed on zooplankton.

8 CORNETFISH or FLUTEMOUTH

Fistularia commersonii

Up to 150cm (4ft 11in). The family *Fistulariidae* are elongated fish with big eyes and slightly flared snouts. This species is silvery in colour, but can change its coloration to mottled to blend with the surrounding reef. The dorsal and anal fins are situated well back on the body, and a whip-like tail extends beyond. *Ecology:* This fish favours flat sandy reefs, where it hovers immobile close to the bottom. It is often found in regions associated with strong currents. The diet of this fish includes small fish and invertebrates.

BARRACUDAS

Family *Sphyraenida*

The family *Sphyraenidae* has a ferocious reputation, which, at least in the Red Sea, is ill-deserved. The body is elongate and silvery, with dark bars. The head is pointed, with a large mouth and fang-like teeth. Larger individuals are solitary in shallow water along reef walls. Smaller species generally form schools, which sometimes number in the thousands, and may be guarded by one or more resident sharks, for example at Ras Mohammed.

1 GREAT BARRACUDA

Sphyraena barracuda

Up to 190cm (6ft 3in). This is the largest of the barracudas, distinguished by a dark tail-fin with pale tips. Teeth are formidable and can potentially inflict a vicious bite. It is an inquisitive animal, though rarely a threat to divers. Its vicious reputation is partly explained by its appearance and partly as a result of injuries to divers engaged in macho barracuda-feeding antics. *Ecology:* Juveniles frequent shallow lagoons and estuaries, while adults are more common in clear seaward waters, where they hunt solitarily and close to the surface.

2 PICK-HANDLE BARRACUDA

Sphyraena jello

  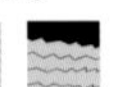

Up to 150cm (4ft 11in). This barracuda is distinguished by yellowish tinged fins, and a body that tapers slowly towards the head. *Ecology:* It is often found in schools or small groups above shallow current-swept reefs. In the summer, there are several groups resident on reefs in Safaga, and one on Yolande Reef at Ras Mohammed. In the Seven Brothers I have watched them at cleaning stations, swimming head down in the water while the cleanerfish goes about its business.

7 Barred Flagtail

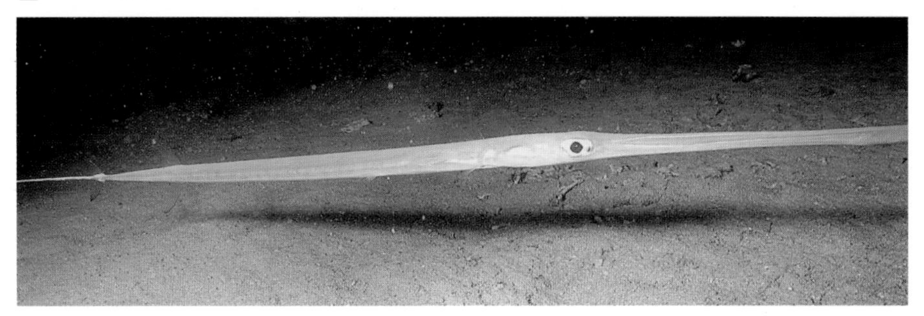

8 Cornetfish

1 Great Barracuda

2 Pick-handle Barracuda

3 YELLOW-TAIL BARRACUDA

Sphyraena flavicauda

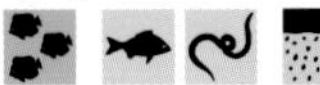

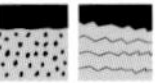

Up to 45cm (1ft 6in). This small species is often mistaken for juveniles of the larger types of barracuda. The body is silvery with two tan stripes, and the tail is yellow. The head comes to a sharper point than other species. *Ecology:* Yellow-tail barracudas prefer shallow bays and lagoons of seaward reefs. Here, they can shelter from the current while still having access to their preferred prey. They form large schools, which at night put on an impressive display of panic and confusion under the torch beam.

4 BLACK-FIN BARRACUDA

Sphyraena quenie

Up to 160cm (5ft 3in). This species is identified by the dark dorsal, anal and tail fins. The body is patterned with dark bands. *Ecology:* It forms large densely packed schools above current-swept reefs and drop-offs. It is this species that forms a school of thousands in the summer off Ras Mohammed. A diver entering the school is often chased back out by any one of a group of several Oceanic Black-tip Sharks and Silky Sharks that consider this food source their own.

FUSILIERS

Family *Caesionidae*

Fusiliers are responsible for the immense blue schools that hover off most Red Sea reefs. They are similar to snappers with their continuous dorsal fins, broad forked tails, rounded heads and coarse scales. But they are generally smaller, have long protrusible mouths for eating plankton and are predominantly blue. By night, they hide in the reef to sleep, at which time they take on a deep red hue. Fusiliers are an important food fish for snappers, trevallies, barracudas, sailfish and many other semi-pelagic species. In the Red Sea, the Bedouin use them as live bait to catch these large predators.

1 LUNAR FUSILIER

Caesio lunaris

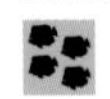

Up to 25cm (10in). The Lunar Fusilier appears much 'bluer' than the other species, although final identification comes from the blue tail lobes, which lack white markings. *Ecology:* This species forms dense schools in open water, where it feeds on plankton. Diving among them can be one of the Red Sea's most hypnotic experiences. It also occurs in mixed schools, although it is often segregated slightly further offshore than other fusiliers.

2 SUEZ FUSILIER

Caesio suevica

Up to 25cm (10in). This fusilier is distinguished from related species by a fine yellow stripe along each dorsal flank and white edges to the black tips of the tail lobes. *Ecology:* In the north, this is the most common of the Red Sea fusilier species. It forms mixed schools in mid-water along reef slopes and drop-offs, where it feeds on plankton.

3 STRIATED FUSILIER

Caesio striata

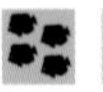

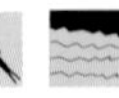

Up to 20cm (8in). The pale blue body is striped with black along the dorsal flanks. The tail lobes are also streaked black. *Ecology:* Juveniles cling close to the reef slopes, forming a dense blue haze. Adults form large schools in open water, but are still tied to the reef. It is particularly abundant in the southern Red Sea and is not found far north of the border between Sudan and Egypt.

3 Yellow-tail Barracuda

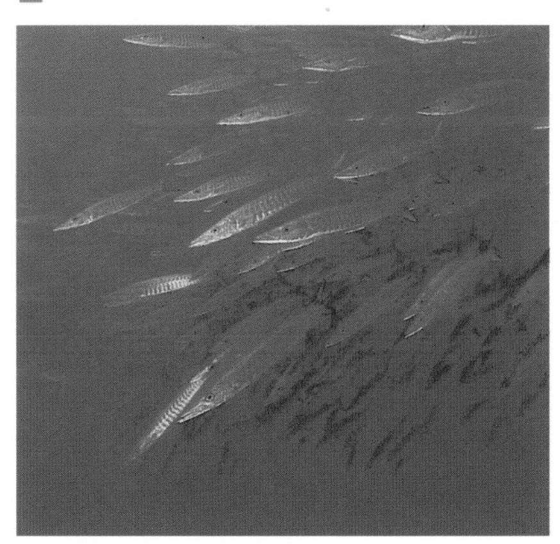

4 Black-fin Barracuda

1 Lunar Fusilier

2 Suez Fusilier

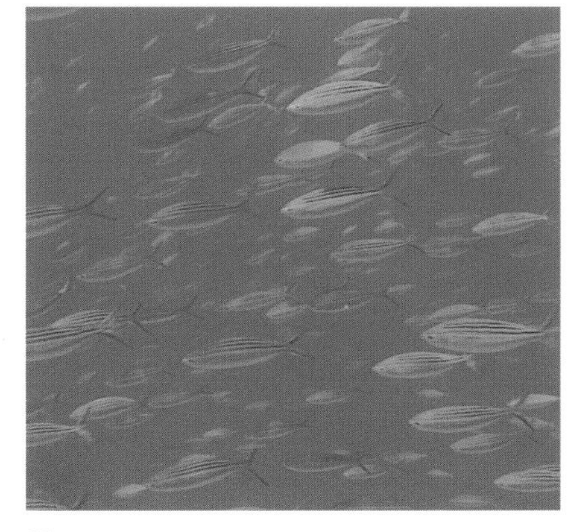

3 Striated Fusilier

SNAPPERS

Family *Lutjanidae*

Snappers are solid medium-sized fish, with broad forked tails, large coarse scales, rounded heads and continuous dorsal fins. They can be solitary, but are mostly schooling fishes. It is the Twin-spot Snapper that in summer forms the huge and well-photographed school at Ras Mohammed. Even before diving began, this school was famous throughout the Arab world and Bedouin fishermen would come from as far as Saudi Arabia to join the harvest.

1 TWIN-SPOT SNAPPER

Lutjanus bohar

Up to 90cm (2ft 11in). This coppery-brown fish gets its name from two white dorsal spots that are particularly evident in the juvenile. *Ecology:* This powerful and voracious predator can be seen roving along seaward coral slopes or forming immense schools, usually in areas of heavy current. It feeds on small fish such as fusiliers, as well as crustaceans and cephalopods. I once witnessed two of these fish separate a fusilier from its school. They then bumped it between them, disorientating it, before tearing it apart. The whole process took just a couple of seconds.

2 HUMP-BACK SNAPPER or PADDLE-TAIL SNAPPER

Lutjanus gibbus

Up to 50cm (1ft 8in). A distinctly humped back and paddle-shaped tail distinguish this fish from the Twin-spot. The coloration is silver with reddish-brown and black fins. *Ecology:* It is uncommon north of Sudan, but fairly well distributed in the deep south. In Egypt, distribution is coastal and mostly south of Marsa Alam. It is occasionally solitary, but more often seen in large schools. It feeds on benthic fish and invertebrates.

3 ONE-SPOT SNAPPER

Lutjanus monostigma

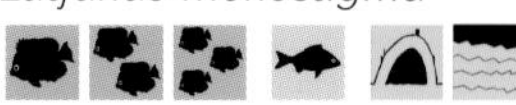

Up to 60cm (2ft). This medium-sized species is silver with orange fins and a single black spot just beneath the dorsal fin. *Ecology:* This species is shy and solitary, usually seen lurking in caves and beneath table corals, and is difficult to approach. It feeds on small fish, usually by night.

4 BLACK-SPOT SNAPPER

Lutjanus fulviflamma

Up to 35cm (1ft 2in). This species is similar in form and in colour to the One-spot, but it differs by having yellow longitudinal stripes along its flanks and is usually somewhat smaller. It is more similar to *L. ehrenbergii*, but can be distinguished by its extra yellow stripe just above the pelvic and anal fins. *Ecology:* This fish often mixes with schools of the Blue-striped Snapper above seaward reefs with mild current. It is fairly evenly distributed throughout the Red Sea.

5 BLUE-STRIPED SNAPPER

Lutjanus kasmira

Up to 35cm (1ft 2in). Four black-bordered longitudinal blue stripes are arranged on a yellow background. The belly is white. *Ecology:* This species is usually found in immense schools on shallow sandy reefs. These schools are often of mixed species, including other snapper species as well as goatfish species. The inner reefs of Safaga bay, for example, are ideal territory. The schools disperse at night to feed on crustaceans.

6 BLACK SNAPPER

Macolor niger

Up to 65cm (2ft 2in). The coloration is mottled dark grey or black. The head is rounded and the dorsal and anal fins are markedly flared. *Ecology:* This species forms small groups in shallow water along seaward reef walls. In particular, it prefers bays where it can gain shelter from currents. A large group may be found on the seaward side of Tiran's Thomas Reef and in southern Egypt there is barely a reef that does not have a group.

1 Twin-spot Snapper

2 Hump-back Snapper

3 One-spot Snapper

4 Black-spot Snapper

5 Blue-striped Snapper

6 Black Snapper

SWEETLIPS

Family *Haemulidae*

This family is very similar in appearance to the snappers. The scales are coarse, the head is rounded and the dorsal fin is continuous. The mouth, however, is smaller, with large fleshy lips, and it is positioned lower. The tail is not forked like that of the snapper, and the general appearance is less dynamic. By day they are inactive, sheltering beneath overhangs and table corals, only emerging at night to feed.

1 BLACK-SPOTTED SWEETLIPS

Plectorhinchus gaterinus

Up to 45cm (1ft 6in). The body is silvery-grey with black spots on the dorsal flanks, but the overall impression is yellow. The fins are yellow and the anal, dorsal and caudal fins are black-spotted; the fleshy lips are also yellow. Juveniles are black and yellow striped. *Ecology:* This species forms small, tight groups that shelter beneath table corals and in hollows of seaward reef slopes by day. There is often a strange symmetry to the group, typically stacked nose to tail in a cuboid formation.

2 SILVER SWEETLIPS

Diagramma pictum

Up to 75cm (2ft 6in). This stocky fish is silvery, sometimes with dark grey smudges on the body. The head is also dark grey. The body is very deep. *Ecology:* It favours inshore reefs and lagoons where, in small groups or pairs, it roves across sand or weed beds in search of invertebrate prey. It sometimes forms mixed groups with other species such as snappers, especially in the northern Red Sea where it is uncommon. This picture was taken among the old containers on the wreck of the *Yolande*.

SPADEFISH

Family *Ephippidae*

Also known as batfish. They have extremely deep, laterally compressed bodies, and high fins. The juveniles, which live in mangroves and lagoons, have even deeper bodies and higher fins than the adults. They usually roam in small groups, or can form impressive schools. They are extremely inquisitive, often following divers for the duration of a dive, or approaching to peer into their masks.

1 CIRCULAR SPADEFISH

Platax orbicularis

Up to 57cm (1ft 10in). The adults are almost circular with a silvery body. One dark band runs vertically across the eye, and another just behind the gill flaps. The forward fins are tinged yellow. Juveniles are darker with taller dorsal and anal fins. The Long-fin Spadefish *P. teira* is almost identical, distinguished by a dark blotch just before the anal fin. *Ecology:* Because they prefer lagoons and mangroves, the juveniles are rarely seen by divers, but the adults are a common and unmistakable sight. They feed on algae, invertebrates and small fishes.

1 Black-spotted Sweetlips

2 Silver Sweetlips

1 Circular Spadefish, adult

1 Circular Spadefish, juvenile

EMPERORS AND BREAMS

Lethrinidae and *Sparidae*

Emperors are another snapper-like group of fish. Like the snappers, they have continuous dorsal fins, coarse scales and broad, forked tails. Unlike the snappers, however, their snouts are generally pointed and their faces tend to have a straight or concave profile. They typically stay close to the reef by day, resting in sheltered water. By night, they feed aggressively on crustaceans, sand-dwelling invertebrates and small fish. They are important food fishes especially *Lethrinus mahsena* (mehseny in Arabic), and *L. nebulosus* (Sha-or in Arabic). Breams are a similar family, which feed exclusively on benthic invertebrates, as are *Nemipteridae*, the threadfin breams.

1 ARABIAN THREADFIN BREAM

Scolopsis ghanam

Up to 20cm (8in). This species is pale with chocolate-brown stripes dorsally, which give way to brown spots on the flanks. *Ecology:* This is one of the most common threadfin breams, and although three other species exist in the Red Sea, they are hardly ever seen. It hunts for small invertebrates, and also takes large zooplankton.

2 DOUBLE-BAR BREAM

Acanthopagrus bifasciatus

Up to 50cm (1ft 8in). This species is uniformly silver with twin vertical black bars on the face. The pectoral, dorsal and caudal fins are tinged with yellow and the inner lips are tinged with blue. *Ecology:* This bream is seen singly or in loose groups in shallow water. It tends to shelter in the bays of seaward reefs, often in mixed schools with emperors and snappers, as shown in the picture. It feeds on a wide variety of benthic invertebrates.

3 BIGEYE EMPEROR

Monotaxis grandoculis

Up to 60cm (2ft). This silvery snapper-like fish is identified by the steep head profile, large eyes and yellow tinged lips. The pectoral fins are usually tinged with pink. Juveniles are dark with white bars. *Ecology:* This fish is sometimes solitary but is more frequently found in small groups, drifting motionless in the shallow waters alongside seaward reefs. These schools disperse at night to feed on benthic invertebrates.

4 MAHSENA EMPEROR

Lethrinus mahsena

Up to 65cm (2ft 2in). This olive and silver-barred fish has fins tinged with red. It is larger than most other emperors, with a heavier, blunter head. *Ecology:* It is usually seen in twos or threes on seaward reef slopes, where it feeds upon echinoderms and crustaceans. It is an important food fish for the Bedouins, who are careful to avoid the semi-toxic dorsal spines when catching it.

5 BLUE-SPANGLED EMPEROR

Lethrinus nebulosus

Up to 80cm (2ft 7in). This beautiful pale fish has dramatic electric blue markings on the face and dorsal flanks. The face has a distinctly concave profile. *Ecology:* This emperor occurs singly over sand or seagrass beds, where it feeds by ambushing crabs, molluscs and other benthic fish. Like the Mahsena Emperor it is an important food fish for locals. This picture shows the survivor of an unsuccessful attack, probably by a shark.

6 LONG-NOSED EMPEROR

Lethrinus olivaceus

Up to 100cm (3ft 3in). The body colouring is a mixture of silvery and dusky scales, which may be arranged indistinctly or in a mottled pattern. It is easily recognized by the elongate face and sleek body form. *Ecology:* Its diet is less invertebrate-based than the other emperors. It uses guile and speed to take bottom-dwelling fish, squid and octopus.

1 Arabian Threadfin Bream

2 Double-bar Bream

3 Bigeye Emperor

4 Mahsena Emperor

5 Blue-spangled Emperor

6 Long-nosed Emperor

UNICORNFISH, SURGEONFISH AND TANGS

Family *Acanthuridae*

This family is recognized by the oval body shape and the scalpel at the base of the tail, which is often highlighted with a bright colour. The scalpel is used purely as a means of defence. They are herbivorous fish, grazing on algae from the reef surface and, for this reason, several species are very common on reef flats or on wrecks, where algae grows abundantly.

The subfamily *Nasinae* is more commonly known as the unicornfish. They have two scalpels on the tail and, in most species, a nasal spike or at least a lump. Unlike the surgeonfish and tangs, they are schooling fish, often seen in open water where they feed on plankton.

1 SLEEK UNICORNFISH, BLACKTONGUE UNICORNFISH or BLUE-KEEL UNICORNFISH

Naso hexacanthus

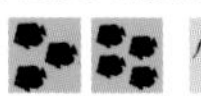

Up to 75cm (2ft 6in). The body is classically fish-shaped, dusky in colour, with a yellow underbody. The blue coloration only takes over when being cleaned at cleaner stations or during courtship displays. *Ecology:* This fish usually forms vast schools in open water. In the southern Red Sea these schools often range very deep and are guarded by Silver-tip Sharks. It feeds on the larger forms of zooplankton.

2 BLUE-SPINE UNICORNFISH or SHORTNOSE UNICORNFISH

Naso unicornis

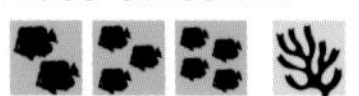
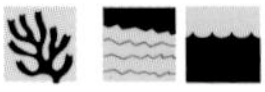

Up to 70cm (2ft 4in). This fish is uniformly olive in colour, with two distinct blue spines at the base of the tail. *Ecology:* This species is usually seen in small dense schools in areas of intense current (for example at Ras Mohammed). It also favours shallow surgy waters along reef edges, where it feeds on benthic brown algae.

3 LONG-NOSE UNICORNFISH or SPOTTED UNICORNFISH

Naso brevirostris

Up to 60cm (2ft). The colouring in this species is grey or olive with a pale band behind the gills, and with dark spots all over. The 'horn' is considerably longer than that of the related Blue-spine Unicornfish. *Ecology:* This fish favours seaward reef slopes and especially drop-offs with a steady current. Adults are usually seen in open water, rising and falling on the current, and feeding on zooplankton. Juveniles feed on benthic algae.

4 ORANGE-SPINE UNICORNFISH or YELLOW-KEEL UNICORNFISH

Naso lituratus

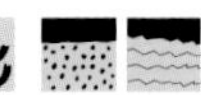

Up to 50cm (1ft 8in). The body is black, fading to grey on its dorsal surfaces. The dorsal fin and two spines at the base of the tail are coloured yellow or orange. *Ecology:* This striking species is often seen in pairs, roaming sandy reefs, and shallow reef walls. It is particularly common in the region of Hurghada. It feeds on benthic brown algae.

5 BLACK SURGEONFISH or MONK TANG

Acanthurus gahhm

Up to 40cm (1ft 4in). The ovaloid body is very laterally compressed, and is black in colour with a white band at the base of the tail. *Ecology:* This fish forms loose groups over sandy reefs. It is an inquisitive fish and often follows divers, attacking their bubbles. It is found throughout the Red Sea, but is much more prolific in the south than the north.

1 Sleek Unicornfish

2 Blue-spine Unicornfish

3 Long-nose Unicornfish

4 Orange-spine Unicornfish

5 Black Surgeonfish

6 SOHAL SURGEONFISH
Acanthurus sohal

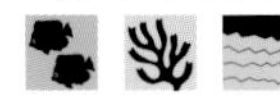

Up to 40cm (1ft 4in). The pale grey body is marked with black lines and an orange patch behind the pectoral fins. The tail spine is blaze-orange. *Ecology:* This fish inhabits reef flats and shallow wrecks, which it guards territorially, protecting its algae from other grazers.

7 SAIL-FIN TANG or INDIAN SAILFIN TANG
Zebrasoma desjardinii

Up to 40cm (1ft 4in). This fish is dark in colour with faint diagonal bars. The dorsal and anal fins are continuous and very tall. *Ecology:* This species prefers seaward reefs, where it is often seen in pairs, grazing on algal growths.

8 BLUE SAIL-FIN TANG or YELLOWTAIL SURGEONFISH
Zebrasoma xanthurum

Up to 25cm (10in). This fish is uniformly royal blue in colour, with a gold tail and pectoral fins. Dorsal and anal fins are enlarged and continuous. *Ecology:* This species is usually seen either singly or in pairs on seaward reefs. It feeds by grazing benthic algae from the reef. It is widely distributed throughout the Red Sea.

9 STRIPED BRISTLE-TOOTH TANG
Ctenochaetus striatus

Up to 26cm (10in). The body and head are dark brown in colour. *Ecology:* This species favours reef-flats and lagoons, but also seaward reefs, where it grazes algal turfs.

RABBITFISH
Family *Siganidae*

Siganidae are ovaloid fish, with small terminal mouths. The spines of the dorsal and anal fins are thick and sharp, and can inflict a painful, although not dangerous, wound. They are herbivorous fish, feeding mainly on benthic algae, which they graze from the reef top.

1 SILVER RABBITFISH or FORKTAIL RABBITFISH
Siganus argenteus

Up to 42cm (1ft 5in). This species is pale grey with yellow pectoral fins and yellow forehead. *Ecology:* It is most common in the south. It usually roams in small schools over seaward reefs and areas of coral rubble

2 RIVULATED RABBITFISH or RED SEA RABBITFISH
Siganus rivulatus

Up to 30cm (1ft). The olive markings of this species are dappled across a sandy coloured body. *Ecology:* This fish sometimes occurs singly, but it usually forms large schools, favouring seagrass beds. It is also seen over sandy reefs, as in this photograph taken on a night dive in El Quesir. At this site, it grazes benthic algae.

3 STELLATE RABBITFISH or BROWN-SPOTTED RABBITFISH
Siganus stellatus

Up to 40cm (1ft 4in). This distinctive species is pale with dense black spots, yellow-tinged fins and a yellow forehead. *Ecology:* It is usually found in pairs. It is well distributed throughout all types of reef habitat where there are benthic algae to be grazed.

6 Sohal Surgeonfish

7 Sail-fin Tang

8 Blue Sail-fin Tang

9 Striped Bristle-toothed Tang

1 Silver Rabbitfish

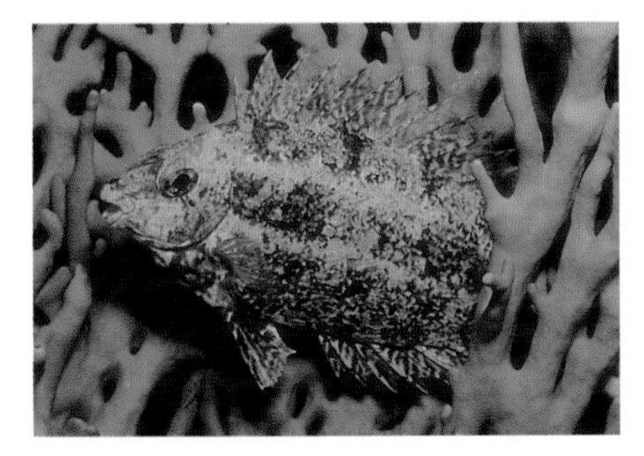

2 Rivulated Rabbitfish

3 Stellate Rabbitfish

TRIGGERFISH AND FILEFISH

Family *Balistidae*

Triggerfish are laterally compressed fish, with deep bodies, large heads and high set eyes. The mouth is situated terminally, and is small with large chisel-like teeth. The tail is well armoured and therefore useless for swimming. Instead, the flexible dorsal and anal fins are undulated, providing a unique and characteristic swimming motion.

In all triggerfish species the first dorsal fin forms a spike, which is raised as a warning of imminent attack, or fully erected as a camming device to lock itself in crevices when under attack itself. If caught, this spike can be unlocked by pressing on the second dorsal spine. They are volatile fish, especially the Titan Triggerfish, which in late summer poses a considerable threat to divers, inflicting nasty bites and, according to anecdotal evidence, at least once knocking a diver cold. The appropriate response is to move away since they are only protecting their eggs, which are laid in a depression in the sand. Triggerfish feed on a wide range of invertebrates.

Filefish *Monacanthidae* are closely related, but are more delicately built than the triggerfish. They also feed on invertebrates, although some have specialized to take corals and plants too.

1 **TITAN, GIANT** or **MOUSTACHED TRIGGERFISH**

Balistoides viridescens

Up to 75cm (2ft 6in). Body colour varies between olive and pale orange, patterned with dark scales. A dark band extends across the upper lip, and from the eyes down to the pectorals. The dorsal, anal and caudal fins are pale with black outer and inner edges. The tail is lined with harsh spines. *Ecology:* This fish is notorious as the most aggressive creature in the Red Sea. Its reputation is well earned in the months of July, August and especially September, when it protects its nest from all intruders, including divers. The only sensible response is flight, though sideways rather than up.

2 **ARABIAN PICASSOFISH**

Rhinecanthus assasi

Up to 30cm (1ft). This distinctive little fish is pale grey, with unique blue, yellow and red markings. The lips are large and fleshy, and are bright yellow. *Ecology:* This species occurs singly or in pairs over sandy reefs. It rummages through the sand, searching out crustaceans and worms. It is widely distributed through the Red Sea, and is especially common in the north.

3 **RED-TOOTH TRIGGERFISH**

Odonus niger

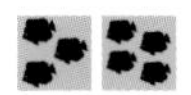

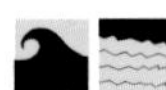

Up to 40cm (1ft 4in). This medium-sized fish is deep blue in colour, with a distinctive 'swallow-tail'. The face is sometimes paler than the body, and the most distinguishing feature is the teeth, which are blood-red and fang-like. It is not to be confused with the Blue Triggerfish, which is larger and lacks the red teeth. *Ecology:* This fish usually forms vast loosely packed schools, which rise and fall on the current. When startled it retreats into holes for protection, leaving only its tail protruding.

4 **BLUE TRIGGERFISH** or **PAINTED TRIGGERFISH**

Pseudobalistes fuscus

Up to 55cm (1ft 10in). This large triggerfish is deep blue in colour, and sometimes blotched with pale green. It should not be confused with the Red-tooth Triggerfish, which is a smaller species with red teeth. *Ecology:* The Blue Triggerfish lives almost exclusively in sandy lagoons and on sandy patches of seaward reefs. It is usually seen head-down, blowing into the sand to unearth worms and crustaceans. It is common and widely distributed. Only very rarely is it aggressive towards divers.

1 Titan Triggerfish

2 Arabian Picassofish

3 Red-tooth Triggerfish

4 Blue Triggerfish

5 YELLOW-MARGIN TRIGGERFISH
Pseudobalistes flavimarginatus

Up to 60cm (2ft). The body colour of this solid fish varies between stone and olive. The face is stained red, giving the impression of a hyena or lion feeding at a kill. All the fins are dark with a golden outer margin. *Ecology:* This is a solitary fish that resides over sandy reefs and in sandy lagoon channels. It often grows larger than the Titan Triggerfish, but is never the dominant species in a confrontation. It feeds on benthic invertebrates and tunicates. It is common throughout the Red Sea, and in Egypt is found as far north as Hurghada, but is absent from the offshore islands.

6 WHITE-TAIL TRIGGERFISH
Sufflamen albicaudatus

Up to 30cm (1ft). This species is brown with an orange tail with white markings. It is very similar to the Half-moon Triggerfish, *S. chrysopterus*, for which it is commonly mistaken, but it can be distinguished by the white band at the base of the tail. *Ecology:* This common species is found on most mixed or sandy reefs, for example Shark Bay in the Sinai, where this picture was taken. It feeds on a wide range of invertebrates.

7 ORANGE-STRIPED TRIGGERFISH or YELLOWTAIL TRIGGERFISH
Balistapus undulatus

  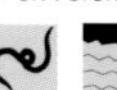

Up to 30cm (1ft). This triggerfish is cobalt-blue in colour with gold stripes, which are lost from the snout in adult males. The tail and all other fins are gold. *Ecology:* This triggerfish is common throughout the Red Sea, on all types of reef, from sandy plateaus to rocky walls. It feeds on a variety of urchins, molluscs and crustaceans.

8 BLUE-SCRIBBLED FILEFISH
Aluterus scriptus

Up to 100cm (3ft 3in). Electric-blue markings are 'scribbled' across a pale grey or stone coloured body. The body is much more elongated than in other filefish or triggerfish. The snout is long and upturned, and the first dorsal spine is elongated. *Ecology:* This shy, solitary species is common throughout the Red Sea. It feeds on a wide range of plants and animals, from gorgonians and fire corals to tunicates. I once watched one floundering at the surface, as a large predator surged around beneath, eventually demolishing it.

9 BROOM FILEFISH
Amanses scopas

  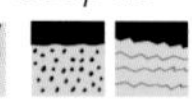

Up to 20cm (8in). This is a small, dusky fish, with orange fins. Towards the tail, females have dense 'brooms' of setae, which project outwards from the body. In males these setae are replaced by five or six thick spines. *Ecology:* This species, which is usually seen in pairs, is extremely wary of approaching divers, usually rushing for cover among the corals. It is widespread, ranging from the Gulf of Aqaba, where this picture was taken, to the deep south. It feeds on a variety of invertebrates.

10 RED SEA LONGNOSE FILEFISH
Oxymonacanthus halli

  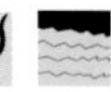

Up to 7cm (3in). This tiny filefish is unmistakable: turquoise with dense yellow spots. The snout is long, upturned and bright yellow. The pelvic fins are orange. *Ecology:* This fish is usually found in pairs on shallow *Acropora* coral reefs, the polyps of which it eats. The reefs north of Hurghada appear to be good territory for spotting these uncommon creatures.

5 Yellow-margin Triggerfish

6 White-tail Triggerfish

7 Orange-striped Triggerfish

8 Blue-scribbled Filefish

9 Broom Filefish

10 Red Sea Longnose Filefish

BOXFISH AND TURRETFISH

Genus *Ostraciidae*

The three species that inhabit the Red Sea are typical of the genus *Ostraciidae*. They have cuboid bodies encased in a box of fused bony plates. This box is actually the skeleton, and one can occasionally find them washed up on the beach – a sad, but strangely comical sight. Gaps are left in the armour for the mouth, eyes, gills, fins, tail and anus. The mouth is generally downturned and trunk-like, lending this genus its other name – trunkfish. They swim by beating the dorsal and anal fins, reserving the hinged tail for a burst of speed when threatened. All three species are protected to some extent by a toxin secreted from the skin. They feed on algae and sessile invertebrates.

1 ARABIAN BOXFISH or BLUETAIL TRUNKFISH

Ostracion cyanuruas

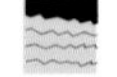

Up to 15cm (6in). This is the smaller of the two species of Red Sea boxfish. The male is characterized by blue sides and belly, with a green dorsal surface. The female varies between black with white spots, and yellow with black spots. The mouth projects downwards, and is almost trunk-like. *Ecology:* This tiny fish is a solitary inhabitant of rich seaward coral reefs, rarely venturing far from cover. It is awkward to approach, and often corners itself in holes, peering out at the diver.

2 CUBE BOXFISH or YELLOW BOXFISH

Ostracion cubicus

Up to 11cm (4½in). Females are yellowish in colour. Males vary between grey and brown with blue and black spots. The mouth projects downwards and above it is a nose-like knob. *Ecology:* This species prefers seaward reefs with dense coral growth to provide shelter. Despite its appearance, it can put on an impressive burst of speed when threatened (although that is no excuse for harassing it). It is widely distributed throughout the Red Sea, from the coast of the Sinai, where these pictures were taken, to the deep south. It is protected by a toxic layer of mucus, released from the skin, which is presumably derived from its diet of algae.

3 HUMP-BACK TURRETFISH or PYRAMID BOXFISH

Tetrasomus gibbosus

Up to 30cm (1ft). The body is cuboid, but tapers towards the top, and is capped with a pointed 'blade'. The coloration is mottled grey, with electric-blue scribbles. *Ecology:* This bizarre creatures tends to shun coral reefs in favour of seagrass beds, sandy slopes or algae covered reef-flats. It has little need of coral cover since it is protected by poisonous 'ostracitoxin', which is secreted from its skin. It seems especially prolific in the less interesting dive sites such as Na'ama Bay in the Sinai, or around any jetty (the grottier the better).

1 Arabian Boxfish

2 Cube Boxfish, female

2 Cube Boxfish, male

3 Hump-back Turretfish

PORCUPINEFISH AND PUFFERFISH

Family *Tetraodontidae*

This family is known as *Tetraodontidae*, meaning 'four toothed', and is characterized by the teeth being fused to form a powerful beak. This beak is used to break open hard-shelled molluscs and crustaceans, or the fingers of foolish divers who try to molest them. As a rule, they are left alone by predators because of their ability to increase their own size by inflating. In porcupinefish, this defence is reinforced by a coat of sharp spines. Although divers find it amusing to goad this fish into inflating itself, it should be left alone. If it inflates itself at the surface, it is unable to pump the air back out, as it can with water, and it will roast to death in the sun.

This family is also toxic and the tetrodotoxin is fatal to humans if eaten. Nevertheless, they are a delicacy in the Far East, where they are specially prepared (*see* p.8).

1 COMMON PORCUPINEFISH

Diodon hystrix

Up to 90cm (2ft 11in). The largest of the porcupinefish is grey with small black spots. The spines are moveable, and usually lie flat, but are erected only when threatened. *Ecology:* It is reclusive by day, emerging by night onto shallow reefs to feed on a wide range of hard-shelled creatures, which it breaks open with its powerful jaws. It is this species that has been known to remove the fingers of divers who harass it in the hope of seeing it inflate. The juveniles are said to be pelagic.

2 MASKED PORCUPINEFISH, BLACK-BLOTCHED or SHORTSPINE PORCUPINEFISH

Diodon liturosus

  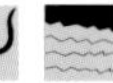

Up to 65cm (2ft 2in). This medium-sized fish is tan or olive-green, with white-ringed, black blotches all over its body. A broad black stripe masks each eye. *Ecology:* This species is widespread and common in the Red Sea, but is rarely seen owing to its reclusive nature. At night, it emerges to feed on a range of molluscs and crustaceans.

3 YELLOW-SPOTTED PORCUPINEFISH

Chilomycterus spilostylus

  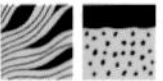

Up to 34cm (1ft 1in). This species is much like the Common Porcupinefish in appearance, but it has white spots on a dark background, as opposed to dark spots on a pale background. *Ecology:* This is another shy species, which is active by night over a wide range of habitats, feeding on molluscs and crustaceans, which it dismantles with its powerful jaws. It favours sandy reefs and seagrass beds. This picture shows a fish that has been harassed into puffing itself up – a practice that is not recommended.

4 WHITE-SPOTTED PUFFER

Arothron hispidus

  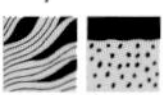

Up to 40cm (1ft 4in). White spots mark a body that varies in colour between grey and brown. Most striking, are the bold white rings around the eyes and the pectoral fins. *Ecology:* This solitary fish can be found across a wide range of habitats from rubble slopes to seagrass beds. Here, it feeds on assorted plants and invertebrates, which are broken up with its powerful jaws.

5 STAR PUFFER or GIANT PUFFER

Arothron stellatus

Up to 120cm (3ft 11in). The largest of the puffers is pale with black spots and a white underbelly. Juveniles are more orangey with dark blotches, which merge to form bands across the belly. *Ecology:* Juveniles prefer weedy lagoons and sheltered reefs. Adults are more common on clear, seaward reefs, where they are often found resting on sandy patches, and are slow to move off. This species has a diverse diet, including sponges, corals and invertebrates.

1 Common Porcupinefish

2 Masked Porcupinefish

3 Yellow-spotted Porcupinefish

4 White-spotted Puffer

5 Star Puffer

6 MASKED PUFFER
Arothron diadematus

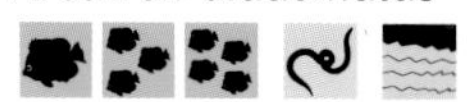

Up to 30cm (1ft). Pale grey with black spots. It has a bold, black mask, snout and pectoral fins. It is similar in form to the Black-spotted Puffer, *A. nigropunctatus*, but the mask is more defined. *Ecology:* This species is usually solitary, except during courtship, when it forms large schools roaming along the reef. A notable site for this phenomenon is Ras Mohammed. It is widespread throughout the Red Sea, and favours reefs with rich coral growth.

7 CROWN TOBY or CROWNED SHARPNOSE PUFFER
Canthigaster coronata

Up to 14cm (5½in). This tiny creature is white or grey with four black dorsal 'saddles'. It is similar in appearance to the Black-saddled Toby, *C. valentini*, but the saddles are less pronounced. The eyes are gold, green and very striking. *Ecology:* This fish is usually solitary or paired, on seaward reefs. It favours areas of shale and rubble, where it grazes benthic algae or hunts invertebrates.

8 PYGMY TOBY or DWARF SHARPNOSE PUFFER
Canthigaster pygmaea

Up to 6cm (2½in). The tiny beige or pinkish body is spotted blue towards the back, and vertically striped with blue towards the front. *Ecology:* This uncommon fish is extremely reclusive, rarely venturing outside of reef crevices. It appears to be fairly well distributed throughout the Red Sea. This picture shows this species reclining in the shelter of a sponge.

GROUPERS

Family *Epinephelinae*

Groupers are the archetypal reef predators. They feed by ambushing smaller fish and crustaceans. They are generally mottled in colour to blend with the surroundings and have an oversized caudal fin to propel them swiftly on to their prey. The Giant Grouper is the largest of all reef fishes, weighing up to 400kg (880lb). Like all the larger grouper species it is fairly shy and retiring. Smaller species are important food fish for Red Sea locals and, although larger fish are not ciguatoxic as they are in other parts of the world, they are not good to eat.

1 GIANT GROUPER
Epinephelus lanceolatus

Up to 300cm (9ft 10in). This monster has dark olive coloration, mottled with black. All the fins are tipped with yellow. Juveniles are black with yellow and white blotches. *Ecology:* This is the largest coral reef fish, and easily outweighs a man. It is found primarily in the South, especially Yemen, in wrecks and caves, although it has been seen as far north as the *Thistlegorm*. Larger individuals are generally shy, but cannot overcome their natural curiosity and have a nasty habit of sneaking up on divers from behind. There are even unconfirmed fatal attacks by this species, probably when speared. It feeds on lobsters, fish, sharks and turtles.

2 POTATO GROUPER
Epinephelus tukula

Up to 200cm (6ft 7in). This is a stocky fish with a large, bullish head. Its coloration is sandy, with widely-spaced dark blotches. *Ecology:* This species favours shallow sandy reefs such as those in the Gulf of Suez. It feeds mainly on fish, and is hand-fed in many parts of the world, although fortunately not in the Red Sea.

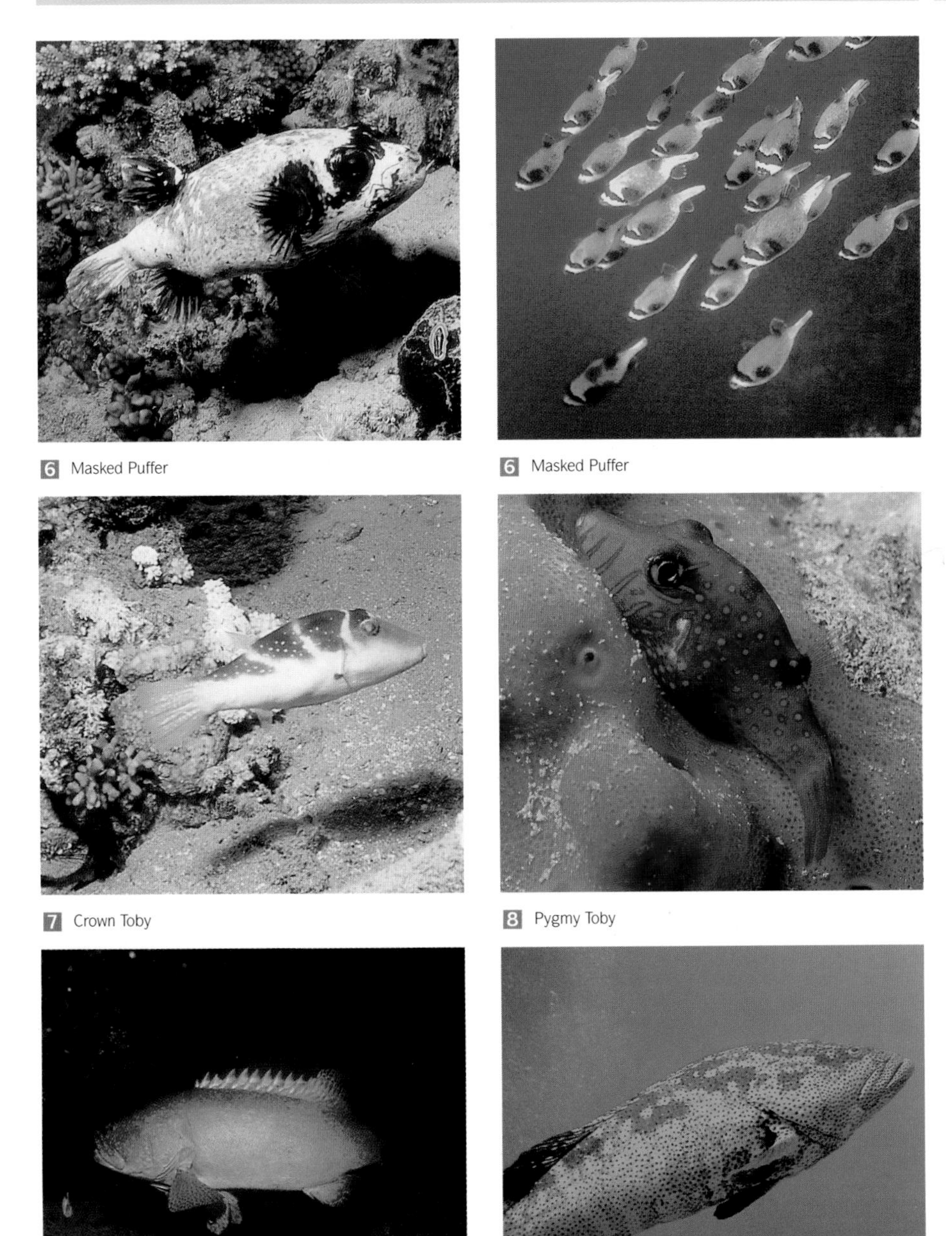

6 Masked Puffer

6 Masked Puffer

7 Crown Toby

8 Pygmy Toby

1 Giant Grouper

2 Potato Grouper

3 MARBLED GROUPER

Epinephelus polyphekadion

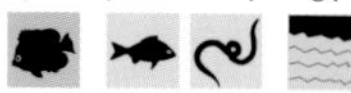

Up to 75cm (2ft 6in). This beautiful fish is fawn in colour with patches of light and dark grey. Like the rest of its family, it can grow to impressive dimensions. It is generally smaller than the Brown-marbled Grouper and is otherwise distinguished by its straight, uninterrupted head profile. *Ecology:* The Marbled Grouper is most commonly found in the central areas of the Red Sea (Sudan and Southern Egypt). In all circumstances it is a fairly shy and retiring fish, rarely venturing far from a suitable bolt hole. It feeds on fish and crustaceans.

4 BROWN-MARBLED GROUPER or BULLHEAD COD

Epinephelus fuscoguttatus

  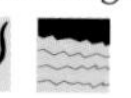

Up to 90cm (2ft 11in). This is another solid fish, although it is generally smaller than the closely related Malabar Grouper, *E. malabaricus*. It also differs from this species by having a distinct dip in the forehead, below which is a broad snout. The coloration is pale brown with rough vertical stripes of dark brown towards the tail. *Ecology:* It is more common in the southern than the northern Red Sea on seaward coral reefs and islands. It feeds mainly on crustaceans and occasionally on fish.

5 GREASY GROUPER

Epinephelus tauvina

Up to 75cm (2ft 6in). This medium-sized fish is much paler than other related groupers. Brown spots are arranged on a cream background. The fins are also spotted with dark edges to the posterior fins. *Ecology:* This species rarely ventures far into the open. Instead it lurks under coral overhangs on seaward reefs, waiting to ambush crustaceans and fish. It is widely distributed, and appears to be very prolific in the region of Safaga, where this photograph was taken.

6 SNOWFLAKE GROUPER or SUMMANA GROUPER

Epinephelus summana

Up to 52cm (1ft 8in). Large, white, snowflake-like blotches are arranged against a dark, speckled background. *Ecology:* This fish is widespread throughout the Red Sea on shallow sheltered reefs. It is often active in the open by day. In Safaga I have frequently seen it schooling alongside other fish, such as sweetlips and snappers – unusual behaviour for groupers, which are usually solitary.

7 RED SEA CORAL-GROUPER

Plectropomus marisrubri

   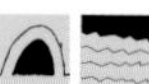

Up to 110cm (3ft 7in). Also known (incorrectly) to local guides as the Leopard Grouper or as the Squaretail Grouper. The chunky body is pale with six or seven dark-brown interconnected bars. All the fins are dark brown, and the entire fish is covered with blue spots. There is a closely related species, the Roving Coral-grouper, *P. pessuliferus*, which is red with blue spots and lacks the dark bars of the Red Sea Coral-grouper. *Ecology:* These two types of fish are very common in the Red Sea, especially in the north, although rare throughout the rest of their range. They are usually seen lurking inside caves or beneath overhangs, or moving through dense coral cover. Both are frequent visitors to cleaning stations, where they hang motionless with their mouths open, until the cleanerfish is done. They feed on a wide range of fish and crustaceans.

8 RED-MOUTH GROUPER

Aethaloperca rogaa

Up to 60cm (2ft). The dark-brown body is much deeper than that of other groupers. The inside of the mouth is bright scarlet and a pale band sometimes marks the flanks. *Ecology:* This fish lurks in deep caves and wrecks, where it preys on Glassfish, among other species. It rarely leaves the darkness, but is tempted out when anthias prove irresistible when they are forced to hug the reef for shelter from strong currents.

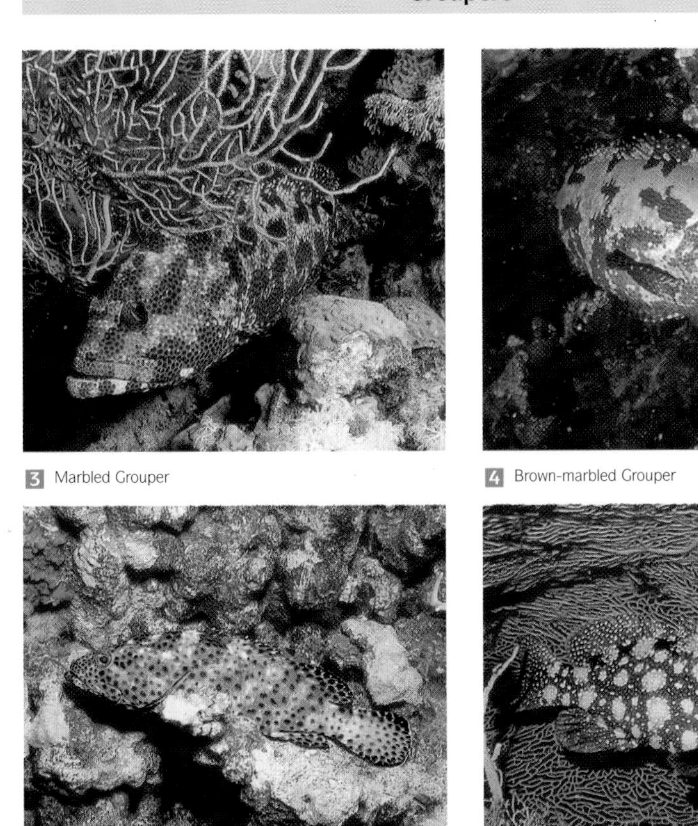

3 Marbled Grouper

4 Brown-marbled Grouper

5 Greasy Grouper

6 Snowflake Grouper

7 Red Sea Coral-grouper

8 Red-mouth Grouper

9 LYRE-TAIL GROUPER, LUNARTAIL or MOON GROUPER

Variola louti

Up to 80cm (2ft 7in). Blue spots cover a violet or carmine body. The caudal fin is sickle-shaped, and edged with gold, as are all the other fins. The juvenile is white ventrally, pink dorsally, with a bold black lateral line. *Ecology:* This beautiful fish is extremely common in the northern Red Sea, where it patrols in the open, over seaward reefs. It has a diverse diet of fish, crustaceans and other invertebrates, which the Bedouins say give its flesh extra flavour.

10 BLACK-TIP GROUPER or RED-BARRED ROCKCOD

Epinephalus fasciatus

Up to 40cm (1ft 4in). This grouper is pale red with broad dark-red bars. All fins are red, and the dorsal fin has a black outer margin, sometimes with white tips to the spines. *Ecology:* This is a common fish in all reef habitats in the northern Red Sea. It inhabits shallow water, and reef tops, and is therefore easily caught by the Bedouins, who value it as an eating fish. It feeds on a wide range of fishes and crustaceans.

11 CORAL HIND or JEWEL GROUPER

Cephalopholis miniata

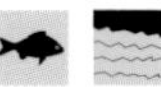

Up to 40cm (1ft 4in). This small grouper is scarlet with blue spots. The dorsal, anal and caudal fins sometimes have a black and blue border. *Ecology:* This species is very common on rich seaward reefs with clear water. On Jackson Reef in Tiran, for example, it is packed one fish to almost every crack or crevice. It hunts voraciously on small fish, and seems especially active when the current is running strong and the anthias are forced to swim close to the reef for shelter, making them especially vulnerable to attack.

12 SIX-SPOT GROUPER or SADDLE GROUPER

Cephalopholis sexmaculata

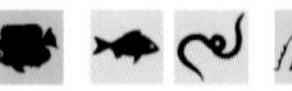
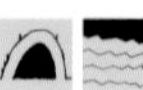

Up to 47cm (1ft 6in). This species is red with six dark bars along body. It differs from *E. fasciatus*, which also has dark bars along the body, by a covering of bright blue spots. The caudal, dorsal and anal fins have blue borders. It is also similar to the Coral Hind, but is distinguished by the blue lines on the head and the dark bars on the body. *Ecology:* This is a common species in the north, favouring caves and crevices. It feeds on small fish, and occasionally crustaceans.

13 RED SEA HIND or HALF-SPOTTED HIND

Cephalopholis hemistiktos

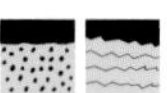

Up to 35cm (1ft 2in). Coloration in this species is variable, from dark red to pale olive with bars. The body is blue-spotted ventrally, as is the face, but the upper body is clear red. The caudal fin is dark with a pale blue border. *Ecology:* This is a widespread species that is more commonly found on sandy and mixed reefs than the coral-rich reefs favoured by *C. miniata*. It feeds on a wide range of fish and crustaceans.

14 PEACOCK GROUPER

Cephalopholis argus

Up to 40cm (1ft 4in). This small grouper is dark brown or olive becoming progressively pale towards the tail. The body is covered with blue spots, which are especially dense on the fins. Some individuals may have broad white bars towards the tail. *Ecology:* This attractive species prefers coral-rich reefs, where it hunts out small fish and, to some extent, invertebrates. Juveniles favour the shelter of reef-top lagoons and shallow coral thickets. It is well distributed throughout the north and the south of the area.

9 Lyre-tail Grouper

10 Black-tip Grouper

11 Coral Hind

12 Six-spot Grouper

13 Red Sea Hind

14 Peacock Grouper

HAWKFISH

Family *Cirrhitidae*

This family is named after one distinguishing feature – the small hairs or 'cirri' which sprout from the ends of each dorsal spine. Hawkfish are all predators, behaving much like tiny groupers. They rest motionless during the daytime on coral outcrops.

1 FRECKLED HAWKFISH

Parachirhites forsteri

  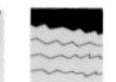

Up to 22cm (8½in). The belly is pale yellow or white, and the back is brown or even red. The face is usually a paler shade of brown with deep red freckles. The caudal fin is broad, and usually yellow. *Ecology:* Common on seaward reefs in the north, with clear water and rich coral growth. It perches motionless above coral outcrops, waiting to ambush small fish and occasionally shrimps.

2 SPOTTED HAWKFISH

Cirrhitichthys oxycephalus

Up to 10cm (4in). The belly is white and the back pale grey, both being adorned with large dark-centred red blotches. *Ecology:* This species favours coral-rich seaward reefs with clear water. It perches above corals, attacking small shrimps or fish that happen by. It is widespread although generally uncommon, ranging from Egypt, where this picture was taken, to as far south as the Indian Ocean.

3 LONGNOSE HAWKFISH

Oxychirrhitus typus

Up to 12cm (4½in). This species is white with a dense lattice of red lines. It usually keeps its tall, spiky dorsal fin erect, and also has a distinctive long snout. *Ecology:* This uncommon species is found only in gorgonian corals and black corals. Here, it feeds on small crustaceans that live within the branches, or large zooplankton that have become trapped by them.

MORAYS

Family *Muraenidae*

The moray family has a much maligned, although undeserved reputation, which is undoubtedly the result of their ferocious snake-like appearance. Without doubt, divers have been severely bitten by them in the past, but only when the morays have been pulled from their holes to act as props for moray-wrestling photographs.

Morays are differentiated from other eel families by the pronounced dorsal and anal fins running the length of their bodies, and by the lack of pectoral fins. The scaleless skin is well supplied with mucus, which helps their snake-like gliding through the coral undergrowth. They use their excellent sense of smell to hunt out sleeping reef fish at night.

1 GIANT MORAY

Gymnothorax javanicus

    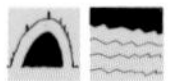

Up to 300cm (9ft 10in). This formidable creature is brown in colour, with rows of black spots and leopard-like blotches. It can grow to an immense size, in both length and girth, and is commonly thicker than a man's leg. *Ecology:* This is the most common moray in the Red Sea. It lurks in caves and beneath boulders on seaward reefs. It has become very abundant where fed by divers, such as on Carless Reef in Hurghada. Hand-feeding morays looks impressive but is unwise. It disrupts the ecology and teaches morays to approach divers, which can cause novices to panic.

1 Freckled Hawkfish

2 Spotted Hawkfish

3 Longnose Hawkfish

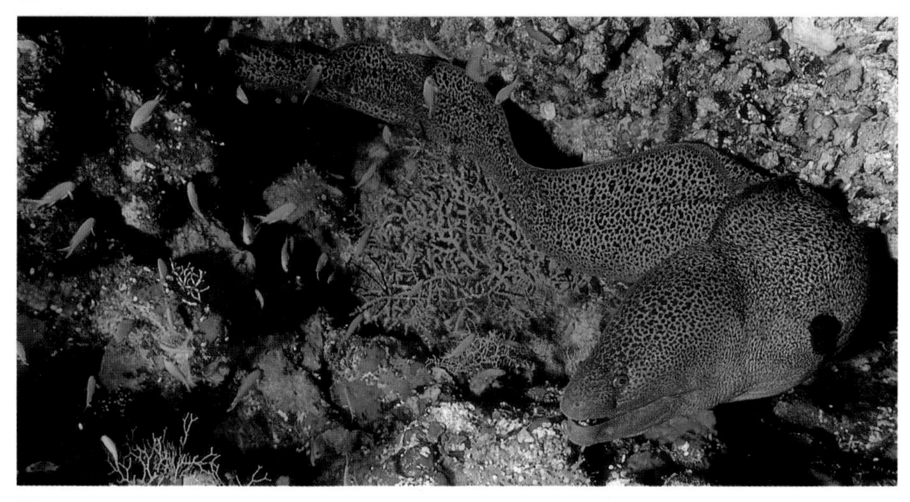

1 Giant Moray

2 YELLOWMOUTH MORAY
Gymnothorax nudivomer

Up to 180cm (6ft). This moray is light brown with black-ringed white spots, which are closely spaced on the head and widely spaced towards the tail. It has a dramatic yellow mouth, and can grow to a respectable size. Its skin is protected by toxic mucus. *Ecology:* This moray is rare throughout the Red Sea, although probably less rare in the north. This photograph was taken at Taba in the Gulf of Aqaba, which seems to be a good location for rarities, probably because of the cool water.

3 YELLOW-MARGINED MORAY
Gymnothorax flavimarginatus

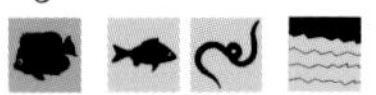

Up to 120cm (3ft 11in). This eel is similar to *G. javanicus*, although it is generally smaller. The snout is dark and the body is brown, mottled with yellow. The eyes are yellow. *Ecology:* This is one of the more common morays on sandy reefs. It is a voracious hunter of reef fish, and is often active in the open by day. When approached, it will rapidly make for cover, lodging itself in a hole and gaping aggressively. It is probably more common in the northern Red Sea than in the south.

4 HONEYCOMB MORAY
Gymnothorax favagineus

    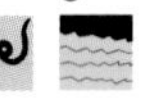

Up to 250cm (8ft 2in). This is the only other Red Sea moray that grows to the same proportions as the Giant Moray. It is sandy coloured, with densely packed black blotches. *Ecology:* This handsome animal is found only in the deep south, being fairly prolific in the Seven Brothers in the straits of Bab El Mandeb, and in the Hanish Islands of Yemen. It is not found north of Eritrea. This eel is a voracious predator on seaward reefs with strong current. It is less dependent on coral cover than the Giant Moray and often roams in the open, putting on an aggressive display towards approaching divers.

5 UNDULATED MORAY
Gymnothorax undulatus

Up to 150cm (4ft 11in). The Undulated Moray is distinguished by its pointed head and long jaw. It is mottled and yellowish in colour, and the body is yellow interspaced with darker blotches. *Ecology:* This is a rare species in the Red Sea and is hardly ever seen, as it hides deep within the reef. At night, it emerges to feed on fishes, octopuses and crustaceans. It is aggressive, but shy towards divers, retracting into its hole if a camera strobe goes off, and not emerging for a long time.

6 YELLOW-HEADED MORAY
Gymnothorax ruppelliae

Up to 60cm (2ft). This is a slim moray with a yellow head and darkly barred body, although the coloration is often very faint, as in this picture. *Ecology:* This species hides deep in the reef by day and is usually seen at night, when it is nervous and aggressive towards divers. It prefers sandy reefs, where it hunts small fishes and crustaceans. Shark Bay in the Sinai seems to be a prime location for spotting these creatures.

7 SNOWFLAKE MORAY
Echidna nebulosa

Up to 80cm (2ft 7in). This moray is usually quite small with a blunt, rounded head. It is pale with yellow-spotted dark blotches. *Ecology:* This moray is rare in the Red Sea, but occurs over a wide range of reef habitats. In particular, it favours reef-tops where it emerges at night to hunt, and its choice of this habitat makes it especially unlikely to be seen by divers. I have never seen one in the Red Sea, though as the photograph was taken there, it clearly does exist there. Its diet is mainly based on crustaceans.

2 Yellowmouth Moray

3 Yellow-margined Moray

4 Honeycomb Moray

5 Undulated Moray

6 Yellow-headed Moray

7 Snowflake Moray

8 PEPPERED MORAY

Siderea grisea

Up to 40cm (1ft 4in). This small white moray is patterned with tiny, widely-spaced, black spots on the head. The head is fairly blunt and rounded. *Ecology:* This is a common species on sandy reefs throughout the Red Sea, although somewhat more prolific in the north. It is usually solitary, but can occur in small groups, especially when young. It is usually confined to a hole by day but emerges fully at night to feed on small fish. This species often accompanies hunting packs of Yellow-saddle Goatfish, *Parupeneus cyclostomus*. They take advantage of the chaos to snap up occasional reef fish that have been forced from their holes by the unruly pack. Although small, the Peppered Moray will readily nip the finger of an interfering diver, as I once learned to my embarrassment while leading a group of students on a night dive. Once attached, they are extremely difficult to remove.

OTHER EELS

The conger family is represented in the Red Sea by only one species *Conger cinereus*, which is generally found on sheltered reefs and in deep lagoons. The majority of congers occur in temperate waters, favouring wrecks and boulder-strewn reefs with ample cover. Congers are generally more cylindrical than the morays, which are slightly laterally compressed.

Unlike all other eels, the garden eels (*Heterocongridae*) are effectively sessile. They form colonies, living in deep burrows excavated in fine coral sand often at great depth. They choose sand patches that are well exposed to current and feed by stretching up into the water column to snatch at passing plankton. As a diver or predatory fish approaches, they retract into their holes, only re-emerging once the threat has passed, and because of this shy behaviour are rarely seen in any detail. It is noteworthy that they can distinguish the movements of predators from those of other sand-dwelling fish such as tilefish and razorfish.

1 MOUSTACHE CONGER

Conger cinereus

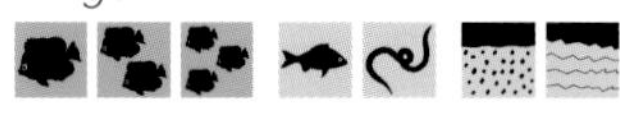

Up to 100cm (3ft 3in). This eel is uniform brown in colour, with a pale belly and a dark 'moustache' on its upper lip. *Ecology:* This species inhabits holes, singly or in small groups. It is found in most habitats, although it is not a familiar species to divers as it shows a preference for reef-flats and shallow lagoons – habitats divers rarely visit.

2 RED SEA GARDEN EEL

Gorgasia sillneri

Up to 42cm (1ft 5in). The body is pale, and slightly freckled. The curvature of the neck is typically more extreme than in other related species. The Spotted Garden Eel, *Heteroconger hassi*, is a similar fish, but is white with black freckles and has a black blotch behind the gills. *Ecology:* It forms dense schools of many thousands in patches of coarse current-washed sand. Larger specimens take the centre of the sand patch, where the sand is deepest.

3 STRIPED CATFISH EEL

Plotosus lineatus

Up to 30cm (1ft). Of the thousands of species of catfish, only a few inhabit saltwater, and of those only two can be found in the Red Sea. The Striped Catfish Eel is characterized by bold dark stripes alternating with white. The snout is fringed by eight white barbels. *Ecology:* Adults are solitary, hiding under coral ledges. Juveniles form dense balls, which swirl about over sandy bottoms.

8 Peppered Moray

1 Moustache Conger

2 Red Sea Garden Eel

3 Striped Catfish Eel, juveniles

4 REEF CUSK EEL or BEARDED BROTULA

Brotula multibarbata

   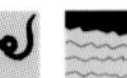

Up to 35cm (1ft 2in). This fish is uniform brown in colour, with a fringe of white barbels around its mouth. *Ecology:* This species is fairly uncommon in the Red Sea, a feature accentuated by its reclusive behaviour. By day it hides beneath ledges in lagoons and sheltered shallow reefs, for example those around Sha'ab Abu Nuhas near Hurghada. At night it ventures out to search for food.

LIZARDFISH AND SANDPERCHES

Sinodontidae and *Pinguipedidae*

The lizardfish family are small, torpedo-shaped reef fish, with mottled colouring and mouths full of sharp teeth. They are usually seen resting motionless on coral outcrops, but can put on an awesome burst of speed to snatch smaller fish that pass by. They often rest half hidden in the sand. The sandperches, although superficially similar, are not related to lizardfish, but they have been included here to help comparison.

1 VARIEGATED LIZARDFISH

Synodus variagatus

Up to 20cm (8in). The ground colour is pale grey, with a pattern of brown and rusty-coloured blotches. There is also a degree of blue mottling. The body is slimmer, and the head is narrower and more pointed than that of the Sand Lizardfish. *Ecology:* This fish is usually seen on prominent coral heads, where it waits to ambush passing fish. They will rest motionless when approached, hoping not to be noticed, but then will bolt off when the diver gets close.

2 SAND LIZARDFISH

Synodus dermatogenys

   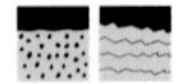

Up to 23cm (9in). This species of lizardfish is usually sandy coloured, with dark grey or brown blotches. Like the Variegated Lizardfish, its mouth is crammed with needle-like teeth, but unlike this species, its head is wide and blunt. *Ecology:* This species is usually seen singly or in pairs. It hugs close to the reef, or buries itself in sand. As prey approaches it launches itself from its resting place to snap the animal up. It is widespread through the length of the Red Sea.

3 SPECKLED SANDPERCH or BLACKTAIL SANDSMELT

Parapercis hexophthalma

Up to 26cm (10in). The sandperches, although superficially similar, are not related to lizardfish. They are represented by only one species in the Red Sea. Its body is sandy coloured with black freckles and a black blotch adorns the caudal fin. The upward-facing eyes are pronounced and the mouth is wide with thick lips. *Ecology:* This is a solitary inhabitant of sheltered, shallow, sandy reefs. It rests patiently on coral outcrops or on the sandy seabed, waiting to ambush passing crustaceans and occasionally fish.

4 Reef Cusk Eel

1 Variegated Lizardfish

2 Sand Lizardfish

3 Speckled Sandperch

SCORPIONFISH AND STONEFISH

Family *Scorpaenidae*

This family *Scorpaenidae* includes a wide range of fish, all of which are venomous. The venom is used defensively and is injected through the dorsal spines, which are stout and pointed with a groove and venom sack. This is only a danger to divers who harass the fish, or who accidentally kneel on them during training exercises or stand on them when entering the water. Both scenarios are easily avoided by staying alert, but in the event of a sting, the affected limb should be treated by immersion in very hot (although not boiling) water, which denatures the protein-based venom. Most of these fish are bottom-dwelling species and rely on highly evolved camouflage to enable them to ambush fish or crustaceans.

1 BEARDED SCORPIONFISH

Scorpaenopsis oxycephala

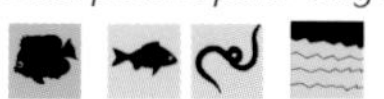

Up to 36cm (1ft 2in). The colour varies between mottled brown and mottled red, according to the background. The large eyes are located on the top of the head and there is a distinct snout, which is fringed along the lower jaw with a 'beard'. The sharp dorsal spines are extremely venomous. The photograph shows a Bearded Scorpionfish in a threat posture, after it has been alarmed by the goatfish on the right of the frame. *Ecology:* This fascinating fish is found in a wide range of habitats, but especially on seaward reefs. Here, it sits perfectly camouflaged on coral outcrops and rubble slopes, waiting to ambush small fish. It is also commonly found on the floors of caves that are inhabited by Glassfish, which serve as a choice meal.

2 DEVIL SCORPIONFISH

Scorpaenopsis diabolus

Up to 22cm (8½in). This brutish looking animal is grey in colour, often with an algal covering on its skin. If threatened it displays bright orange inner pectorals to warn of its venomous sting. The Hump-back Scorpionfish, *S. gibbosa,* is very similar in appearance to *S. diabolus*, but its pectorals are yellower, with a black band and a black submarginal spot. *Ecology:* It is usually seen resting motionless in areas of coral rubble, usually in shallow water. It feeds by ambushing fish and crustaceans.

3 COMMON STONEFISH

Synanceia verrucosa

Up to 38cm (1ft 3in). This grotesque creature varies in colour from grey to lurid pink. It is usually so well camouflaged it can only be discerned by the downturned grimace, or by the widely spaced eyes, which are separated by a deep depression. The long dorsal spines are covered in warty skin and when erected can give a vicious sting. The venom can be fatal. There is a wide degree of variation within this species, from the mossy-looking individual to the lurid pink form. *Ecology:* It is found either half-buried in sand or perched above coral boulders, where it lies in ambush for small fish or crustaceans.

4 FILAMENT-FINNED STINGER

Inimicus filamentosus

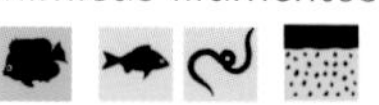

Up to 26cm (10in). The skin of the Filament-finned Stinger is dull and warty. Its head profile is deeply concave, giving it a slightly comical duck-like appearance. The first two or three rays of the pectoral fins are used as legs to crawl across the sand. The bright yellow inner pectorals are flashed as a warning of its nasty sting to potential predators. *Ecology:* This bizarre creature prefers gravelly or sandy bottoms, often lying covered, waiting for prey. Since divers rarely venture far from the reef, this species is perceived to be less common than it really is. It feeds on a range of small fish and invertebrates.

1 Bearded Scorpionfish

2 Devil Scorpionfish

3 Common Stonefish

4 Filament-finned Stinger

5 LIONFISH or TURKEYFISH
Pterois volitans

  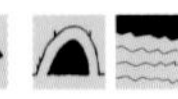

Up to 38cm (1ft 3in). Both the body and the elaborate fins are banded in red-brown and white. The lower jaw is lightly fringed. *Ecology:* This flamboyant animal is the 'Liberace' of the fish world. It is found in all habitats throughout the entire Red Sea. It favours caves, overhangs, and the dark interiors of wrecks. Here, it hunts fish, especially Glassfish, by corralling them using its wide pectorals, often working in groups. It is not intimidated by divers, often swimming arrogantly towards them, refusing to give way.

6 CLEAR-FIN LIONFISH
Pterois radiata

Up to 24cm (10in). Also known (incorrectly) as Turkeyfish. The body is red with white bands. The fin-rays are white with clear fin-membranes. The tail has two horizontal white stripes. *Ecology:* This species is very common in the northern Red Sea. It prefers lagoons and sheltered reefs, where it hides beneath ledges by day, emerging to feed on shrimps and small crabs by night.

7 SHORT-FIN DWARF LIONFISH
Dendrochirus brachypterus

Up to 14cm (6½in). The body is roughly banded, and the pectorals are very striking with bold concentric bands. *Ecology:* This fish is uncommon in the northern Red Sea. It tends to favour coral boulders surrounded by sand, where it hides by day, emerging at night to feed on fish and crustaceans. This photograph was taken in Na'ama Bay in the Sinai: a group of six lionfish had surrounded the anemone, and were attempting to catch the small damselfish within.

OTHER BENTHIC SPECIES

There are numerous other oddly-shaped benthic species in the Red Sea. These include the Seamoth, the White-margin Stargazer, the Painted Frogfish, the Crocodilefish and the Moses Sole.

1 SEAMOTH, PEGASUS or SHORT DRAGONFISH
Eurypegasus draconis

Up to 10cm (4in). This strange creature is generally cryptically coloured to blend with the seabed. The snout is flared upwards, and the tail is curled. It moves by walking with its pectoral fins. *Ecology:* This curious species is usually seen in pairs on shallow gravelly or shaley bottoms, for example in the Canyon lagoon in Dahab or Ras Disha near Safaga. It feeds on tiny invertebrates from within the sand.

2 WHITE-MARGIN STARGAZER
Uranoscopus sulphureus

Up to 35cm (1ft 2in). This lumpy fish has a large head with upward facing eyes and mouth. The pectoral fins are large, and the body tapered. It is sandy coloured above, and white beneath. *Ecology:* It is a solitary hunter, lying concealed in the sand on the reef floor. It attracts small fish using a filamentous dorsal spine as a lure, then lunges from cover to devour them. It is extremely rare in the Red Sea, and I have only ever seen one, on the northern shores of Giftun Kebir in Hurghada

5 Lionfish

6 Clear-fin Lionfish

7 Short-fin Dwarf Lionfish

1 Seamoth

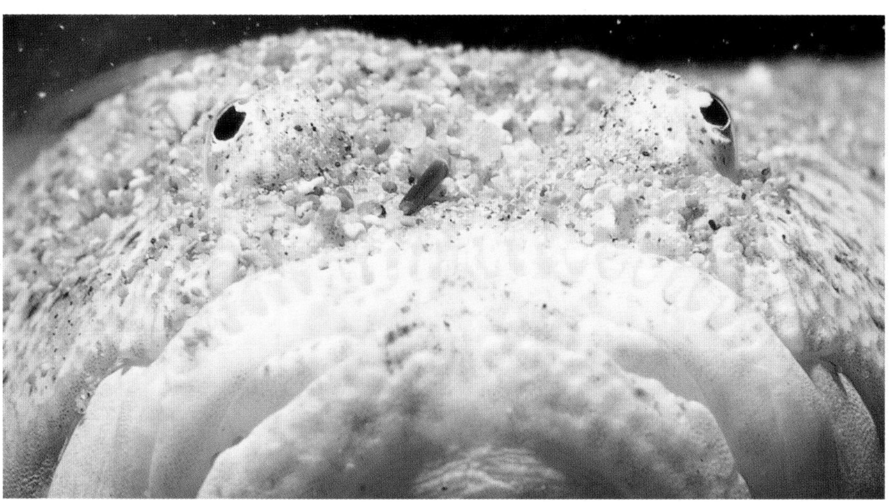

2 White-margin Stargazer

3 PAINTED FROGFISH

Antennarius pictus

Up to 21cm (8½in). This fish comes in a variety of colours from yellow, through red, to black, and it also has various mossy-looking forms. It is a short lumpy fish with a vast mouth and small eyes. The pectoral fins have evolved into legs with a knee-like joint. *Ecology:* This species is rare throughout the Red Sea, being most frequently seen in the Gulf of Aqaba near Nuweiba and Aqaba itself. It is a docile species, which uses its first dorsal spine as a 'fishing rod' to lure small fish. As the fish approach to investigate the lure, they are swallowed in a single, lightning-fast gulp. Surprisingly large prey are taken, including species as unappetizing as Lionfish. When it has chosen a position, this species may remain there for weeks at a time, becoming well known to local guides who often jealously guard the knowledge of their location. A smaller species, the Spotfin Frogfish, *A. nummifer*, also occurs in the Red Sea. It grows to only 10cm (4in) in length, and like the Painted Frogfish it has a wide range of colour forms. All colour variants have one thing in common, however: a dark spot at the base of the dorsal fin. It is rare throughout the Red Sea, although it seems more widely distributed than its larger cousin.

4 CROCODILEFISH or CARPET FLATHEAD

Papilloculiceps longiceps

Up to 70cm (2ft 4in). This fish has a flattened head and body, which is mottled and sandy coloured as camouflage. It has an extremely wide crocodile-like mouth and its eyes, which are positioned high on top of the head, are fringed with long papillae. The inside of its mouth is yellow. *Ecology:* This fish is common throughout the Red Sea, although it is difficult to spot. It lives on mixed sand and rubble, but prefers gravel. Here, it blends with the bottom, often settling beneath the surface, waiting to ambush passing fish or crustaceans. It consumes small fish readily, and although its main diet is said to be cardinalfish, on one occasion I witnessed this species take what appeared to be a bream about the size of my hand. If threatened, this fish rises up on its pelvic fins to show its full size, making it look even more crocodile-like. Individuals seem to keep to a particular location – the wreck of the *Dunraven* in The Gubal Straits has a resident pair, as do many other gravelly locations.

5 MOSES SOLE

Pardachirus marmoratus

Up to 25cm (10in). Juvenile soles start life swimming like any other fish, but as they develop, one eye migrates onto the other side of the body and they start to swim on their sides, taking up a benthic existence. The closely related lefteyed flounders are similar in every way, except that as the name suggests, their eyes are located on the left side of the head rather than the right side, as with soles. This species has an ovaloid body, which is sandy and mottled for camouflage. *Ecology:* The Moses Sole lives on the sandy spaces between reef outcrops to a depth of around 15m (50ft). It is perfectly camouflaged and is rarely seen unless it moves. It secretes a bitter toxin from the base of its dorsal and anal fin rays. This was originally identified as a potential shark repellent by the American marine biologist Eugenie Clark, who was ironically known as 'the lady with the spear'.

3 Painted Frogfish

3 Painted Frogfish

4 Crocodilefish

5 Moses Sole

PIPEFISH AND SEAHORSES

Family *Syngnathidae*

These are tiny elongate fishes, with bodies encased in rings of bony plate. They all have tubular snouts, which are used to suck up invertebrates. The seahorses are upright swimmers, propelling themselves with their dorsal fins, and using their prehensile tails to cling to seagrasses and corals, among which they hide. The pipefish swim horizontally along the seabed, also using their dorsal fins for propulsion.

1 GHOST PIPEFISH

Solenostomus cyanopterus

Up to 16cm (6½in). This fish is uniform brown in colour, varying to green according to its habitat. The fins are oar-like and the snout is elongated. *Ecology:* It is rare in the Red Sea and even where it occurs it is rarely seen, since it blends perfectly into seagrass beds, where it feeds on tiny crustaceans. In its brown form, it also inhabits gorgonians. This photograph was taken close to the seagrass beds in Na'ama bay, Sharm El Sheikh.

2 HARLEQUIN GHOST PIPEFISH

Solenostomus paradoxus

Up to 12cm (4½in). This pipefish is similar in shape to the Ghost Pipefish, but it has tassels all over its body. It is pale in colour, with complex and variable patterns of red and yellow. *Ecology:* It is rare in the Red Sea, hiding in gorgonians, soft corals and among crinoids, where it hunts for tiny invertebrates. It is often found in pairs. This photograph was taken close to Sharm El Sheikh.

3 BLACK-BREASTED PIPEFISH

Corythoichthys nigripectus

Up to 11cm (4½in). The Black-breasted Pipefish is pale in colour with slightly deeper beige bands along its body. The head and flanks are patterned with a fine lattice of blood-red veins. The breast bears a prominent black blotch, and the gill area is also dark. *Ecology:* It favours the shallowest few metres of reef, hiding in cracks and crevices. During egg deposition, the two sexes hover upright in the water, with their tails intertwined.

4 RINGED PIPEFISH

Doryramphus dactyliophorus

Up to 18cm (7in). This species is unmistakable, with its white and chocolate-brown bands running snout to tail. The tail is red and a red line also encircles the eye. *Ecology:* This species is fairly common in the Red Sea but it is rarely seen by divers because it tends to inhabit caves and deep recesses in the reef wall. Its snout is longer than those of other related species and is used to suck tiny cave-dwelling invertebrates from inside narrow cracks.

5 BLUE-STRIPE PIPEFISH

Doryamphus excisus

Up to 7cm (3in). This is the smallest of the Red Sea's pipefish. It is chrome-yellow, with a broad sky-blue stripe running nose to tail. The caudal fin is flared, with red or black mottling on yellow. *Ecology:* This is mainly a cave-dwelling species but it is also seen sheltering among the spines of urchins. There are reports of it acting as a cleanerfish, swimming in a bobbing motion with its tail spread to attract hosts, then moving in and picking out their parasites.

6 THORNY SEAHORSE

Hippocampus histrix

Up to 15cm (6in). Seahorses are represented in the Red Sea by *H. fuscus, H. kuda* and this one. The colour of this species is usually uniform, although it varies between individuals. The edges of the body-plates are distinctly spined. *Ecology:* Seahorses are generally less rare in the Red Sea than one might think. Divers simply pass them by as they are so small and cryptic.

1 Ghost Pipefish

2 Harlequin Ghost Pipefish

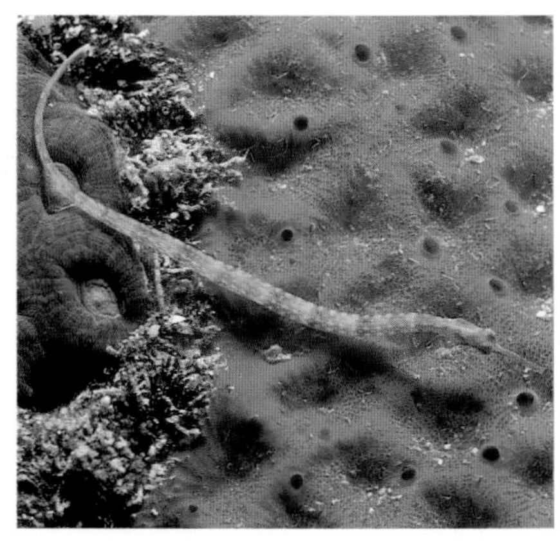

3 Black-breasted Pipefish

4 Ringed Pipefish

5 Blue-stripe Pipefish

6 Thorny Seahorse

SWEEPERS AND CARDINALFISH

Family *Apogonidae*

The sweepers form large schools, which inhabit deep coral caves, or the inside of wrecks. They are small coppery coloured fish with laterally compressed bodies and oversized eyes. Sweepers are popular fish with photographers, making impressive formations as they swoop and swirl in the shafts of light that penetrate the darkness.

Cardinalfish are small reef fish, which live in caves, crevices, or within branching corals or the spines of urchins. They are usually gold or silvery in colour, have large eyes and two dorsal fins.

1 **GLASSFISH** or **RED SEA PYGMY SWEEPER**

Parapriacanthus guentheri

Up to 10cm (4in). This species has a golden body which is slightly transparent. The fins are completely clear and the large eye is golden. *Ecology:* Glassfish preferentially inhabit deep caves in the reef-top, but they will also use wrecks or even overhanging coral-heads. They rely on the confusion of their swirling schools to protect them from their many predators: lionfish, Red-mouth Groupers, trevallies and others. However, they are often no match for the speed of the trevallies, or the cunning of the lionfish, which work in packs, using their wide pectoral fins to corral them and manoeuvre them into an ambush. Each Red Sea resort has its own favourite location for watching these hypnotic creatures, for example Jackfish Alley near Sharm El Sheikh, or Umm Gamar near Hurghada.

2 **HATCHETFISH** or **COPPER SWEEPER**

Pempheris vanicolensis

Up to 18cm (7in). The body is much deeper than that of the Glassfish and it is shaped like the blade of a hatchet. In addition, it is not transparent like the Glassfish, being solid gold or copper in colour. *Ecology:* The Hatchetfish favours deep caves cut into the shallow reef-top. Its schools twist and turn within the darkness, although less maniacally and in lesser numbers than those of the Glassfish.

3 **BROAD-STRIPED CARDINALFISH** or **BLACK-STRIPED CARDINALFISH**

Apogon angustatus

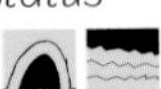

Up to 8cm (3in). The body is patterned with white and deep brown or black stripes of equal width. The base of the tail bears a bold black spot. *Ecology:* This species is found singly or in pairs, sheltering in the cracks and crevices of seaward reefs. It feeds on benthic invertebrates.

4 **ORANGE-LINED CARDINALFISH**

Apogon fucata

Up to 14cm (5½in). The body is gold, fading to white just before a bold black band at the base of the tail, which distinguishes it from The Goldbelly Cardinalfish. Fine orange stripes densely cover the flanks, and three blue stripes mark the face: two across the eye, and one following the upper jaw. *Ecology:* This species is usually seen in small groups, crowding around creviced coral heads in shallow water.

5 **GOLDBELLY CARDINALFISH**

Apogon apogonides

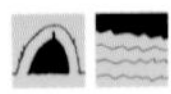

Up to 10cm (4in). This species is gold in colour with a slightly paler belly. Two horizontal blue lines cross the eye, fading into a line of blue dashes down the lateral line. It can be distinguished from the Orange-lined Cardinalfish by the absence of a black band at the base of the tail. *Ecology:* It usually forms pairs, hiding in crevices, soft corals, or among the branches of hard corals. Occasionally it also forms mixed schools with other cardinalfish.

1 Glassfish

2 Hatchetfish

3 Broad-striped Cardinalfish

4 Orange-lined Cardinalfish

5 Goldbelly Cardinalfish

6 TIGER CARDINALFISH or LARGE-TOOTH CARDINALFISH

Cheilodipterus macrodon

Up to 24cm (10in). This large cardinalfish is characterized by broad, wiggly copper-brown stripes, which are wider than the pale spaces between them. The eye is yellow, and the teeth are long. It is the largest cardinalfish to be found in the Red Sea. *Ecology:* This species is usually solitary, favouring reefs with clear water, where it hovers beneath overhangs, and caves. It is a voracious predator of small fish.

BIGEYES, SOLDIERFISH AND SQUIRRELFISH

Holocentridae, Myripristinae and *Priacanthidae*

The *Holocentridae* are all nocturnal fishes with reddish bodies, huge eyes, large scales and deeply forked tails. They are all cave-dwellers that emerge at night to feed. The true soldierfish are smaller than the squirrelfish, with blunter heads and less streamlined bodies. They also lack the venomous pre-opercular spine that characterizes the squirrelfish.

Bigeyes have compressed bodies, large red eyes and large downturned mouths. Although not closely related to squirrelfish and soldierfish, they share many similar characteristics and habitats, so have been grouped together to aid comparison.

1 COMMON BIGEYE

Priacanthus hamrur

Up to 40cm (1ft 4in). This species is unmistakable, with its large red 'goggle-eye' and deep red coloration. *Ecology:* The Common Bigeye prefers seaward reefs, often in exposed locations. It is generally solitary, especially in the north, but occasionally forms large schools, which disperse and rush to the reef for cover on the approach of predators. The north plateau of Abu Kafan in Safaga is one place where such schools are found, as are several of the St John's reefs. It feeds by night on large zooplankton.

2 RED SOLDIERFISH or WHITE-EDGED SOLDIERFISH

Myripristes murdjan

  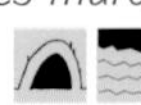

Up to 25cm (10in). The body is silvery-red, and the fins are red with white edges. The large eye is red with a vertical black bar. The Yellowtip Soldierfish, *M. xanthacrus,* is very similar in appearance to the Red Soldierfish, but its dorsal, anal and caudal fins are clearer and are tipped with yellow. *Ecology:* This is the most common soldierfish in the Red Sea. It usually forms small groups, which shelter within caves and beneath overhangs by day. Sometimes, it forms large groups that spill from the shelter of the caves onto the outer reef. It roams the reef at night, feeding on zooplankton.

3 BLOODSPOT SQUIRRELFISH

Neoniphon sammara

  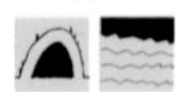

Up to 30cm (1ft). This is a silvery fish with red and black dotted stripes. It is distinguished from other related species by a deep red spot on the forward part of its dorsal fin. *Ecology:* This is one of the more common squirrelfish in some parts of the Red Sea. It tends to be solitary, hiding among the branches of coral bushes, and it is less tied to cover than other similar species. It emerges at dusk to feed on small crustaceans.

6 Tiger Cardinalfish

1 Common Bigeye

2 Red Soldierfish

3 Bloodspot Squirrelfish

4 TAILSPOT SQUIRRELFISH
Sargocentron caudimaculatum

Up to 25cm (10in). The front of the body is generally red, while the rear section is silvery, with a white spot at the base of the tail. A prominent spine extends from the gill flap. The dorsal fin is pale with a dark-red margin. *Ecology:* This species favours caves and crevices on coral rich reef slopes. It is widely distributed throughout the Red Sea, although it is not particularly common.

5 CROWN SQUIRRELFISH
Sargocentron diadema

Up to 25cm (10in). This squirrelfish is red with horizontal silver stripes. The dorsal fin, when extended, is black or deep red with white tips. *Ecology:* This species is equally common both in the northern and southern Red Sea. It is an inhabitant of shallow caves and the crevices of reef flats. It emerges at night to feed on small crustaceans and polychaetes.

6 GIANT SQUIRRELFISH or LONG-JAW SQUIRRELFISH
Sargocentron spiniferum

Up to 45cm (1ft 6in). This is by far the largest of this family. It is a deep bodied fish, which is all red with yellowish fins. The defining feature is a vicious spine that extends backwards from the jaw and can inflict painful wounds. Although not a very scientific characteristic, it is also the most miserable looking of squirrelfish. *Ecology:* This fish is common and widespread, although in areas where shark-feeding used to occur, it is sadly depleted. The reason is that being an unpopular fish because of its miserable-looking face, it has become the main choice as shark bait. It is usually solitary in caves along reef walls, often in exposed environments. It feeds on crabs and other small crustaceans.

DAMSELFISH

Family *Pomacentridae*

The family *Pomacentridae* are small, deep-bodied fish with terminal mouths. They range in diet from the planktivorous *Chromis* species, to the herbivorous *Stegastes* species. Most, however, are omnivores. The algae-feeding species tend to be territorial, and the tiny anemonefish will attack even divers.

1 SCISSOR-TAIL SERGEANT
Abudefduf sexfasciatus

Up to 17cm (6½in). Bold black bars pattern the body of this silvery fish. It is distinguished from other related species by the black fork marking the tail. *Ecology:* Like the Sergeant-major, this damsel occurs in large aggregations in shallow water, feeding on zooplankton, algae and benthic invertebrates. It is widely distributed throughout the Red Sea, and is especially prevalent in the Gulf of Aqaba, where this photograph was taken.

2 SERGEANT-MAJOR
Abudefduf viagiensis

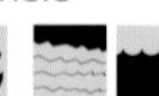

Up to 17cm (6½in). The body is a silver-yellow colour, with bold black bars. The head is grey. It is distinguished from the Scissor-tail Sergeant by the absence of a black V-shape on the tail. *Ecology:* This species is usually seen in large groups in the shallow water along reef edges. There, it feeds on zooplankton, algae and benthic invertebrates. It is widely distributed throughout the Red Sea, perhaps forming the largest aggregations in the north.

4 Tailspot Squirrelfish

5 Crown Squirrelfish

6 Giant Squirrelfish

1 Scissor-tail Sergeant

2 Sergeant-major

3 RED SEA ANEMONEFISH or TWO-BANDED ANEMONEFISH

Amphiprion bicinctus

Up to 12cm (4½in). The body is orange with two white bands, one just behind the eye. The top of the head and the back can be dark brown to varying degrees. *Ecology:* This species is seen singly or in pairs, living alongside a number of different anemone species: *Entacmaea quadricolour*, *Heteractis aurora*, *H. magnifica* and *Stichodactyla gigantea*. It is immensely territorial, attacking approaching fish and even divers, and would probably be a man-eater were it not so small.

4 YELLOW-FIN DAMSEL

Amblyglyphidodon flavilatus

Up to 10cm (4in). This species is grey, with a yellowish tinge on the back and the tail, and it can have a pinkish tinge to the belly. Otherwise it is an indistinct fish, much like the White-belly Damsel. *Ecology:* It is usually seen in large groups feeding on plankton in shallow water, but it is sometimes to be found browsing across the reef for algae and small invertebrates. It is widespread throughout the Red Sea. This picture was taken in El Quesir.

5 WHITE-BELLY DAMSEL

Amblyglyphidodon leucogaster

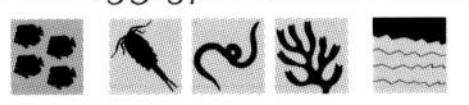

Up to 13cm (5in). This species is uniform silver in colour, although species living in some regions have a belly that is white or even yellow. *Ecology:* It is usually seen in large groups feeding on plankton in shallow water. Alternatively, it is sometimes to be found browsing across the reef for algae and small invertebrates. It is widespread throughout the Red Sea.

6 HUMBUG DASCYLLUS

Dascyllus aruananus

Up to 8cm (3in). The white body bears three bold black lines, which converge to meet at the top edge of the dorsal fin. *Ecology:* This fish is usually found in large congregations above shallow coral heads, especially *Acropora* species. It has a mixed diet of zooplankton, benthic algae and invertebrates. It is a widespread species throughout the Red Sea.

7 RED SEA DASCYLLUS or ARABIAN DAMSEL

Dascyllus marginatus

Up to 6cm (2½in). This fish is creamy coloured, with violet fins, edged with black. *Ecology:* This tiny dascyllus is found on most sheltered reefs and lagoons of the Red Sea. It occurs in pairs or is solitary in shallow, branching corals such as *Acropora, Stylophora* and *Porites*. It feeds on zooplankton, benthic invertebrates and algae.

8 THREE-SPOT DAMSEL

Dascyllus trimaculatus

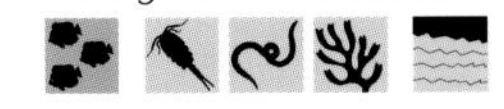

Up to 14cm (5½in). This species is uniformly black or dark grey, with a single white spot on its back. In juveniles, there is a second spot on the forehead, but this still does not explain why it should be called the Three-spot Damsel. *Ecology:* This species is widespread in the Red Sea, with adults congregating around prominent coral heads and rocks. Juveniles are found associated with anemones of the family *Amphiprion*, where they cohabit alongside the Red Sea Anemonefish.

3 Red Sea Anemonefish

4 Yellow-fin Damsel

5 White-belly Damsel

6 Humbug Dascyllus

7 Red Sea Dascyllus

8 Three-spot Damsel

9 SULPHUR DAMSEL

Pomacentrus sulfureus

Up to 11cm (4½in). This small fish is uniformly yellow in colour, with a black base to the pectoral fin. *Ecology:* This species is found on most coral-rich reefs and lagoons of the Red Sea. It is usually solitary, favouring the cover of branching corals such as *Acropora*. It feeds on zooplankton, benthic invertebrates and algae.

10 BLUE-GREEN CHROMIS

Chromis viridis

  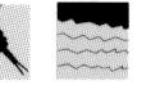

Up to 9cm (3½in). This tiny fish is uniform green or blue green in colour, and has a deeply forked tail. *Ecology:* Juveniles of this species live in heads of branched corals, such as *Pocillopora* or *Acropora* species, above which they hover in groups, bolting for cover when approached. Adults are less tied to a single coral colony, nevertheless staying close above the reef.

11 CHOCOLATE-DIP CHROMIS, TWOTONE CHROMIS or BICOLOUR PULLER

Chromis dimidiata

  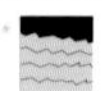

Up to 9cm (3½in). The front half of the body varies between black and dark brown, and the rear half is white. *Ecology:* This small damselfish is abundant on most seaward coral reefs throughout the Red Sea. It is usually seen in large aggregations hovering just above the coral, feeding on zooplankton.

ANGELFISH

Family *Pomacanthidae*

Angelfish are among the reef's most colourful inhabitants. They are medium-sized fish with laterally compressed bodies. They are distinguished from other colourful reef fish by the prominent spine pointing backwards from the gill flap. The many species have a wide-ranging diet, encompassing zooplankton, algae, invertebrates and fish eggs. They are generally solitary, inhabiting mixed coral reefs, and rarely venturing far from some kind of cover.

1 YELLOW-BAR ANGELFISH

Pomacanthus maculosus

Up to 50cm (1ft 8in). This fish is violet or pale purple in colour, with a yellow bar at the centre of its body. The caudal fin is yellow, and the dorsal and anal fins are elongated. The Arabian Angelfish, *P. asfur*, is similar in appearance, but is deeper blue with a bold crescent of yellow splitting the body. *Ecology:* Whereas the Arabian Angelfish is found predominantly in the southern Red Sea in silty coastal habitats, this species inhabits a wide range of reef habitats in the north. It prefers to roam singly over shallow sandy reefs with plenty of available shelter.

2 EMPEROR ANGELFISH

Pomacanthus imperator

  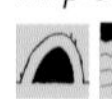

Up to 40cm (1ft 4in). The body is patterned with diagonal yellow and blue stripes, and the face is pale blue and yellow with a black mask. Juveniles are black with concentric white rings. *Ecology:* This fish is reasonably common throughout the Red Sea. It roams singly over seaward slopes of mixed reefs, never venturing far from shelter. Juveniles live inside caves and beneath ledges, so are rarely observed. The sandy reefs that surround the Giftun Islands of Hurghada seem to have more than their share of this species.

9 Sulphur Damsel

10 Blue-green Chromis

11 Chocolate-dip Chromis

1 Yellow-bar Angelfish

2 Emperor Angelfish

3 ROYAL ANGELFISH or REGAL ANGELFISH

Pygoplites diacanthus

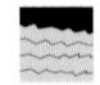

Up to 25cm (10in). Bold yellow, blue and white bars distinguish this species. The juveniles have a similar coloration, but the dorsal fin is yellow with a large blue eye. *Ecology:* It frequents lagoons and seaward reefs, where it occurs singly or in pairs. It usually remains close to cover and often hangs around caves, feeding on sponges and the tips of tunicates.

4 ARABIAN SMOKE ANGELFISH or RED SEA ANGELFISH

Apolemichthys xanthotis

Up to 15cm (6in). A pale body is surrounded by black dorsal fins and a dark head, which bears a yellow spot behind the eye. The caudal fin is yellow. *Ecology:* This species is much more prolific in the north than in the south; this picture was taken in Taba, near Aqaba. It roams in small groups over boulder-strewn reef slopes, grazing on algae, sponges, tunicates and various other invertebrates.

5 ZEBRA ANGELFISH or LYRETAIL ANGELFISH

Genicanthus caudovittatus

Up to 20cm (8in). In males, the body is zebra-striped and the fins are grey, with the dorsal fin bearing a black blotch and the caudal fin elongated with a long trailing edge. Females lack the black stripes and crescent tail of the males. *Ecology:* This fish is usually seen in small groups in the water column above seaward reefs, where it feeds on zooplankton. It is widespread through the Red Sea, and especially common in the Gulf of Aqaba.

BUTTERFLYFISH

Family *Chaetodontidae*

Most member species of the *Chaetodontidae* are yellow, white and black disc-shaped fishes. Some are planktivorous, forming loosely-knit schools over current-washed reefs. Others specialize in feeding on coral-polyps and usually live singly or in pairs, guarding a territory. Others are more generalist, feeding on algae, anemone tips, polychaetes and other sessile invertebrates. The bright coloration is thought to be a signal to other members of the same species, warning them off their territory.

1 THREADFIN BUTTERFLYFISH

Chaetodon auriga

Up to 23cm (9in). This species is predominantly white with black chevron-type markings. The dorsal and anal fins and the tail are yellow. A black mask covers the eye, but the most distinct feature is an elongated extension to the dorsal fin. *Ecology:* This fish prefers sheltered reefs and lagoons, in particular areas of sand and rubble. It feeds by ripping pieces off coral polyps, anemones and polychaete worms.

2 EXQUISITE BUTTERFLYFISH or POLYP BUTTERFLYFISH

Chaetodon austriacus

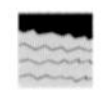

Up to 13cm (5in). This is an oval-shaped fish. It is mainly yellow with dark horizontal stripes dorsally, one bearing a black spot. The dorsal fin is white, while the caudal and anal fins are black. Two bold vertical, black stripes mark the face. *Ecology:* Found singly on sheltered reefs and in lagoons, where it feeds almost exclusively on coral polyps and anemone tentacles.

3 Royal Angelfish

4 Arabian Smoke Angelfish

5 Zebra Angelfish

1 Threadfin Butterflyfish

2 Exquisite Butterflyfish

3 RACOON BUTTERFLYFISH

Chaetodon fasciatus

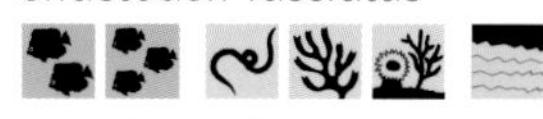

Up to 22cm (8½in). This is another yellow ovaloid fish, but in this case the black stripes are diagonal. A short white stripe marks the forehead, and two black blotches cover the eye and the forehead. *Ecology:* This species is usually seen in pairs or small groups foraging along reef slopes for small crustaceans, polyps and algae. It is one of the most common of Red Sea butterflyfish.

4 LINED BUTTERFLYFISH

Chaetodon lineolatus

Up to 30cm (1ft). This is the largest species of the genus. It is predominantly white with narrow vertical lines. Black bands cross both the eye and the back, and the dorsal, anal and caudal fins are yellow. *Ecology:* A wide range of reef habitats are inhabited by this species, usually in pairs or small groups. It feeds on polyps, algae and the tips of anemone tentacles. It is uncommon but well distributed.

5 BLACK-BACKED BUTTERFLYFISH

Chaetodon melannotus

Up to 15cm (6in). This butterflyfish is not unlike the Lined Butterflyfish in appearance, but it has a yellow face and the black dorsal band extends further. It is also considerably smaller. *Ecology:* This fish prefers sheltered to exposed environments, often roaming singly or in pairs on reef flats. It feeds on a variety of coral polyps, for example on this gorgonian coral on Thomas Reef in the Tiran Straits.

6 CROWN BUTTERFLYFISH or RED-BACK BUTTERFLYFISH

Chaetodon paucifasciatus

Up to 14cm (5½in). The body is white with black chevrons. The face is white with an orange stripe across the eye. The top of the back and much of the dorsal fin is red, as is part of the caudal fin. *Ecology:* This fish is abundant in the southern Red Sea, but less common in the north. It occurs in pairs or in loosely-knit groups, which roam across a wide range of habitats. It feeds on algae, coral polyps, and various invertebrates.

7 MASKED, GOLDEN or BLUE-CHEEK BUTTERFLYFISH

Chaetodon semilardatus

Up to 23cm (9in). This distinctive fish is all-yellow in colour, with a blue cheek-patch. The body is often patterned with vertical lines of dark yellow. *Ecology:* This fish is common throughout the Red Sea. It usually forms large congregations over sandy reefs, or in smaller groups hiding under table corals. The reefs around Hurghada and Safaga appear to be better than most for spotting this fish.

8 LONG-NOSED BUTTERFLYFISH

Forcipiger flavissimus

Up to 22cm (8½in). The face is black above, and white below, with an extremely elongated snout. The body is all yellow, with a black spot at the base of the anal fin. *Ecology:* This odd-looking fish is usually seen in pairs on coral-rich seaward reefs. It uses its long snout to snip out pieces of invertebrates from deep within the reef. It is undoubtedly more common in the south than in the north, although this picture was taken as far north as Ras Mohammed.

9 CHEVRON BUTTERFLYFISH

Chaetodon trifascialis

Up to 18cm (7in). By day, this fish is white with fine black chevron markings; the fins are yellow, the tail is black and a vertical black bar crosses the eye. At night, the body becomes darker with two lateral white spots (*see* picture) *Ecology:* This fish is usually seen singly or in pairs. It guards a territory including *Acropora* corals, on which it feeds, taking the polyps and the mucus. It is fairly common throughout the Red Sea.

3 Racoon Butterflyfish

4 Lined Butterflyfish

5 Black-backed Butterflyfish

6 Crown Butterflyfish

7 Masked Butterflyfish

8 Long-nosed Butterflyfish

9 Chevron Butterflyfish

10 RED SEA BANNERFISH
Heniochus intermedius

Up to 20cm (8in). The butterflyfish family has an elongated fourth dorsal spine, which forms a 'pennant' or 'banner' over the back. All species of this genus, including the two represented in the Red Sea, are patterned with diagonal black and white bands. In this species the dorsal, caudal and pectoral fins are generally yellow. The first black band extends further onto the face than in the Schooling Bannerfish and the overall coloration is more yellow. *Ecology:* This species is often seen in pairs. It also forms schools, but they are never as large as those of the Schooling Bannerfish. It favours flat sandy or mixed coral reefs with mild current.

11 SCHOOLING BANNERFISH
Heniochus diphreutes

Up to 18cm (7in). This fish is distinguished from other related species by having a less pointed snout. The face is much whiter than that of the Red Sea Bannerfish and the second black band ends lower, at the tip of the anal fin. *Ecology:* The Schooling Bannerfish is more prolific in the central and southern Red Sea than in the north. It feeds on zooplankton, and forms large schools numbering in the hundreds. One particularly impressive school occurs on the deep sandy slopes of Tiran's Jackson Reef. It was there that this photograph was taken.

WRASSES

Family *Labridae*

This is one of the most diverse of all reef fish families, varying hugely even within each species as a result of sex change. Typically, both sexes start off drably coloured, some of the females later evolving into brightly coloured males. The family also varies hugely in size from the tiny cleaner wrasse to the mammoth Napoleon Wrasse. One common factor, however, is the use of the pectoral fins for locomotion, except during flight when the tail gives an extra burst of speed. The family's diet is as wide-ranging as its appearance, from urchins and crustaceans to the parasites of other fish. Some species have even specialized in stealing spawn. Larger wrasses such as the Napoleon sleep in home-caves, but most of the smaller species bury under the sand at night.

1 NAPOLEON WRASSE or HUMPHEAD WRASSE
Cheilinus undulatus

Up to 230cm (7ft 7in). As one of the largest reef fishes, its all-green coloration, and the prominent hump on its forehead make this fish unmistakable. *Ecology:* Juveniles gain shelter from clumps of staghorn corals, whereas adults roam freely over all coral habitats. It feeds on a wide range of spiny invertebrates, returning to a home-cave to sleep at night. This species is especially common in the northern Red Sea and, much to its detriment, has been well fed by divers.

2 BROOM-TAIL WRASSE
Cheilinus lunulatus

Up to 50cm (1ft 8in). This gaudily coloured fish has a blunt, rounded head and a deep body. It is distinguished from other wrasses by its blaze-orange pectoral fins and ragged blue or purple tail. Its violent colour-scheme and long flowing tail make this fish the 'drag-queen' of the coral reef. *Ecology:* This species prefers sandy, sheltered reefs, (for example, those in Safaga Bay seem to be a prime spot). It feeds primarily on sand-dwelling invertebrates and urchins, which it breaks up with its rugged teeth.

10 Red Sea Bannerfish

11 Schooling Bannerfish

1 Napoleon Wrasse

2 Broom-tail Wrasse

3 ABUDJUBBE'S WRASSE

Cheilinus abudjubbe

Up to 18cm (7in). The body is pale with dark bars, while the face is green with red lines radiating out from the eye. The colours of this fish are generally mute and washed-out. *Ecology:* This is a common wrasse, which is usually solitary on shallow sandy reefs of the northern Red Sea, for example the reefs of Hurghada, where this photograph was taken. It feeds on invertebrates unearthed from the sand and rubble.

4 RED-BREASTED SPLENDOUR WRASSE or RED-BANDED WRASSE

Cheilinus fasciatus

Up to 38cm (1ft 3in). The face of this species is green, with red lines radiating outwards from the eye. The body is patterned with bold black and white bars and there is a distinctive red blotch around the pectoral fins. This species bears a passing resemblance to Abudjubbe's Wrasse, but the black and white body markings are much bolder. *Ecology:* This species is common in areas of mixed sand and rubble, especially around lagoon patch reefs. Here, it rummages through the sand in search of invertebrates.

5 CHEEK-LINED SPLENDOUR WRASSE or BAND-CHEEK WRASSE

Oxycheilinus digrammus

  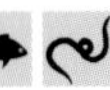 

Up to 30cm (1ft). This species is greeny-blue, with bold pink or red markings radiating outward from the eye. Its belly is flushed red, and its pectoral, dorsal and anal fins are also brightly coloured, varying from gold, through red, to pink. Species of *Oxychelinus* are generally more elongate than those of the closely related *Cheilinus* group. *Ecology:* This fish lives singly over coral-rich areas, both in lagoons and on seaward reefs, where it feeds on a wide range of crustaceans and occasionally fish. It is fairly widespread in distribution.

6 SLING-JAW WRASSE

Epibulus insidiator

Up to 35cm (1ft 2in). Females of this species have striking gold coloration, broken only by a dark eye stripe. Males are black with a red and yellow dorsal patch, and a white or grey mask, which gives them a 'Phantom-of-the Opera'-like appearance. As in the females, a dark line extends backwards from the eye, and the dorsal and anal fins are elongated and flowing. *Ecology:* This species is unique in having a jaw that can extend to half the body length, which it uses to suck up small crustaceans and reef-dwelling fish. From time to time it can be seen stretching this jaw out, possibly to dislodge fragments of food. At this point the mouth looks almost like a proboscis or a trunk.

7 CLOWN CORIS

Coris aygula

  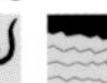

Up to 120cm (3ft 11in). Adult males are characterized by a deep body with a pronounced bump on the forehead. The mouth juts forward with two prominent fangs. Coloration is black with a green or pale blue stripe mid-body, and the tail is ragged. Females are olive-coloured and unremarkable. Juveniles are white with two orange dorsal spots. *Ecology:* This species favours sandy reefs where there is a plentiful supply of hard-shelled molluscs. It also takes urchins and crustaceans, ripping them up with its powerful fangs.

8 CHECKERBOARD WRASSE

Halichoeres hortulanus

Up to 27cm (11in). The head of the Checkerboard Wrasse varies in colour from green with pink facial markings to blue with yellow facial markings. The body, however is unmistakable, being boldly checked in contrasting colours. *Ecology:* Adults of this species favour sandy reefs, where they hunt for small crustaceans hidden within the sand. At night, like its prey, this species buries itself within the sand for protection. In contrast, juvenile Checkerboard Wrasses prefer surge channels on the top of the reef.

3 Abudjubbe's Wrasse

4 Red-breasted Splendour Wrasse

5 Cheek-lined Splendour Wrasse

6 Sling-jaw Wrasse

7 Clown Coris

8 Checkerboard Wrasse

9 RING WRASSE

Hologymnosus annulatus

Up to 40cm (1ft 4in). Adults of this species are green with vertical bands of blue or purple. The face bears several blue markings and the fins are also edged with blue. Its most diagnostic feature, however, is a white vertical band at the centre of its belly. Juveniles are black with white or yellow horizontal stripes top and bottom, and it has been suggested that they mimic the Striped Blanquillo. *Ecology:* This wrasse favours seaward reefs, especially areas of sand and rubble, where it hunts out small fish and occasionally crustaceans.

10 CIGAR WRASSE

Cheilio inermis

Up to 50cm (1ft 8in). The body is much longer and more slender than other wrasse, making this wrasse unmistakable. Coloration is uniformly olive, varying to gold. There are several pale blotches and one dark one behind the gill flap. *Ecology:* This species is found mainly on seagrass beds, where it rummages for invertebrates. It sometimes ventures onto seaward reefs.

11 BIRD WRASSE

Gomphosus caeruleus

Up to 30cm (1ft). The Bird Wrasse is identified by a distinct downturned 'bill'. Males are black with yellow caudal, dorsal and anal fins, while females are dusky brown with pale bellies. *Ecology:* The unique downturned snout is used to probe crevices of the reef for tiny crustaceans. This fish is widely distributed both in the north and the south, favouring coral-rich reefs, such as those of Fury Shoal, where this picture was taken.

12 CHISEL-TOOTH WRASSE

Pseudodax moluccanus

Up to 20cm (8in). The body is grey, with a rusty dorsal fin and shoulder region. The tail is black with a white stripe, and the mouth is bordered by a blue stripe. *Ecology:* Adults inhabit shallow seaward reefs and lagoon channels, while juveniles prefer the deeper waters of drop-offs. The hard protruding teeth are used to dismantle hard-shelled invertebrates.

13 CRESCENT WRASSE or MOON WRASSE

Thalassoma lunare

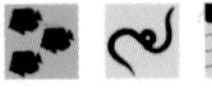

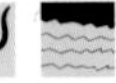

Up to 25cm (10in). The body is green, fading to a blue and pink head. The caudal fin is yellow, within a pink and blue crescent. *Ecology:* This is one of the most common wrasses in the northern Red Sea, favouring mixed seaward reefs, where it roams in haremic groups. It feeds on a wide range of small benthic invertebrates.

14 KLUNZIGER'S WRASSE

Thalassoma klunzigeri

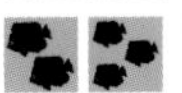

Up to 20cm (8in). The body is pale green with an arrangement of pink bars and stripes. The face is pale with bright pink swirls. *Ecology:* This is one of the most noticeable wrasses along shallow reef-sections of the northern Red Sea, and is easily approached. It favours regions of rich coral growth, usually swimming in pairs. It feeds on a wide range of small benthic invertebrates.

15 BLUE-STREAK CLEANERFISH or COMMON CLEANERFISH

Labroides dimediatus

Up to 10cm (4in). This fish is silvery, fading to blue at the tail. A single broad stripe stretches the length of the body, crossing the eye. *Ecology:* This is the main cleanerfish in the Red Sea. Feeding on the external parasites of larger fish, it advertises its trade through its body coloration and by swimming in a bobbing motion. Potential clients show their intentions by striking unusual poses, such as hovering head down, or by changing their colour, usually to a paler sheen. Once a 'deal' has been struck the recipient will allow the cleanerfish access to its mouth and gill chambers.

9 Ring Wrasse

10 Cigar Wrasse

11 Bird Wrasse

12 Chisel-tooth Wrasse

13 Crescent Wrasse

14 Klunziger's Wrasse

15 Blue-streak Cleanerfish

16 DIANA'S HOGFISH

Bodianus diana

  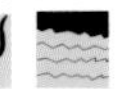

Up to 25cm (10in). This hogfish is pink with a brown head and four or five pale spots along its dorsal flanks. The juvenile is chocolate brown, flecked with white, and the eye is bright red. *Ecology:* This fish is usually seen actively foraging across seaward coral reefs, especially in areas of rubble. The juveniles shelter among soft corals, black corals and gorgonians.

 LYRETAIL HOGFISH

Bodianus anthioides

Up to 21cm (8½in). The front half is rusty brown and the rear half speckled white. The tail has black edges and is crescent-shaped. Adults are very similar to juveniles in appearance, being perhaps whiter towards the tail, and darker brown towards the front. *Ecology:* It is usually seen on the deeper side of reefs, and along drop-offs. All hogfish feed on small benthic invertebrates.

PARROTFISH

Family *Scaridae*

The family *Scaridae* share the same strange sexual development as the wrasses. Both sexes start off life in a drably coloured initial phase, with some of the females switching in their terminal phase into brightly coloured males. Coloration is as striking as in the wrasses, usually in shades of green and pink, but it varies according to sex and age.

Like the wrasses, they generally have cigar-shaped bodies, and swim using their pectoral fins, only resorting to their caudal fins for an extra emergency burst of speed. They are usually solitary or paired, although the Bumphead and Longnose Parrotfish often form large schools. At night, they seek shelter in reef crevices, often cloaking themselves in mucus, presumably to hide their smell from predators.

While the wrasses often have protruding teeth, parrotfish have gone one step further with a strong fusiform beak. This is used to scrape algae from the surfaces of reef-flats, boulders, jetties and wrecks. Some species also consume live coral branches, digesting the polyps, and excreting the rest as coral sand. As such, they are the most important producers of sand on coral reefs. Bear this in mind next time you lie down on the beach.

 LONGNOSE PARROTFISH

Hipposcarus harid

   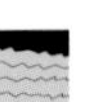

Up to 75cm (2ft 6in). This pretty fish is much paler in colour than any other parrotfish, with a shallower head profile. The caudal fin has elongated margins giving a slightly swallow-tail appearance. The facial markings give this animal a serene smile. *Ecology:* This species usually rummages around singly, but in summer it forms roaming schools of up to 500. At this time, they are usually in a constant state of flight, pursued by predatory trevallies. They are also often seen in groups grazing across the algae-encrusted hulls of wrecks.

 BUMPHEAD PARROTFISH

Bolbometopon muricatum

   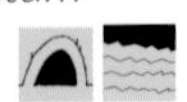

Up to 130cm (4ft 3in). This solid fish is olive in colour, with a pinkish tinge to the face. The forehead is steep, with a pronounced bump. Juveniles are white, with red and black bars on the head and a black spot on the dorsal fin. *Ecology:* The bump on the head is used to ram corals to break them up prior to feeding. Juveniles prefer lagoons but adults are usually found on seaward reef slopes and walls. This species typically roams in large groups, but is also seen singly. It sleeps at night in sandy caves.

16 Diana's Hogfish

17 Lyretail Hogfish, juvenile

1 Longnose Parrotfish

2 Bumphead Parrotfish

3 BICOLOUR PARROTFISH

Cetoscarus bicolor

Up to 90cm (2ft 11in). This striking parrotfish has a far less steeply profiled head than other parrotfish, except perhaps for the Longnose Parrotfish. Males are two-tone green and pink with a pink freckled face, and a long nose. In contrast, females are black with yellow backs and striking gold eyes. *Ecology:* Males are very territorial, protecting a harem of females in shallow sections of seaward reefs, and they are generally very active compared with other parrotfish (which are mostly quite inactive creatures). When roused, males vigorously defend their turf, erecting their dorsal fin, and swimming up and down in territorial displays.

4 RED SEA STEEP-HEAD PARROTFISH

Scarus gibbus

Up to 70cm (2ft 4in). What distinguishes this fish is the steep profile of its forehead, which is almost chisel-like. Males are mottled blue and green, and have bright blue fins and throats. They appear quite different from females, which are gold with green fins and throats. *Ecology:* This classic parrotfish is very common in the northern Red Sea, where it is a voracious feeder on shallow-water corals. The crunching noise when these fish dismantle the reef can be heard metres away.

5 BLUE-BARRED PARROTFISH

Scarus ghobban

Up to 75cm (2ft 6in). This fish is pale blue, mottled with pink. The face, which bears several blue slashes, is also mottled pink. *Ecology:* This is a common parrotfish in the Red Sea and is well distributed north and south, for example at Fury Shoal where this photograph was taken. It is the dominant species in silty environments, such as reef flats and shallow sandy lagoons. It feeds on a mixture of coral and algae.

6 RUSTY PARROTFISH

Scarus ferrugineus

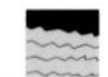

Up to 40cm (1ft 4in). Males are coloured in a mixture of green, blue, orange and pink. In contrast, females are remarkably dull, being brown with orange tails. Given the inequality of looks, it's amazing this species ever manages to pair and mate. *Ecology:* This fish is very common on seaward reefs throughout the Red Sea. It feeds on a mixture of coral and algae, which it scrapes from the reef, using its powerful beak.

7 RED SEA PARROTFISH or DOTTED PARROTFISH

Calotomus virisdiscens

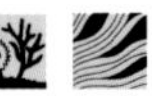

Up to 27cm (10½in). This parrotfish has a mottled olive coloration, with black spots and blotches on the shoulders. The face has distinctive red markings, as do the fins. *Ecology:* This species mainly frequents seagrass beds, where it feeds on the grasses themselves, but it also occurs on coral reefs, where it feeds on epiphytic algae. It is well distributed throughout the Red Sea, but is most common in the north, especially the Gulf of Aqaba.

8 BULLETHEAD PARROTFISH

Scarus sordidus

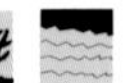

Up to 40cm (1ft 4in). If female Rusty Parrotfish get a rough deal when it comes to looks, then female bulletheads do even worse. Their drab brown coloration is broken only by a white tail band marked with a black spot. Males, on the other hand, are a handsome shade of green, tinged with blue, and have a bright green tail band. *Ecology:* This is one of the Red Sea's most common parrotfish over all kinds of reef habitat.

3 Bicolour Parrotfish, male *(top)*, female *(bottom)*

4 Red Sea Steep-head Parrotfish, male *(top)*, female *(bottom)*

5 Blue-barred Parrotfish

6 Rusty Parrotfish

7 Red Sea Parrotfish

8 Bullethead Parrotfish

GOATFISH

Family *Mullidae*

These medium-sized elongate fish are primarily bottom dwellers. The most distinguishing feature of the *Mullidae* is the twin barbels on their chins, which have a sense of taste and are used to detect prey beneath the sand or within reef crevices. Most feed by day, often working together to flush out prey. They are important food fish on Egypt's Mediterranean coast, although less so in the Red Sea.

1 YELLOW-FIN GOATFISH
Mulloides vanicolensis

Up to 38cm (1ft 3in). This fish is silvery-white with a yellowish back and a bold yellow stripe with blue edges down each side. *Ecology:* This species is widespread throughout the Red Sea, being especially prolific in the north. It forms large inactive schools over sheltered sandy reefs, preferring current-free bays. These schools are often mixed with Blue-lined Snappers. At night, this species disperses across the reef to feed on benthic invertebrates.

2 YELLOW-SADDLE GOATFISH
Parupeneus cyclostomus

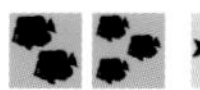   

Up to 50cm (1ft 8in). This medium-sized fish can either be deep gold in colour, or a mixture of violet and yellow. The two barbels are more obvious than on other goatfish. *Ecology:* This fish is common throughout the Red Sea, especially on coral-rich seaward reefs with strong current. It forms small unruly packs, which scour the reef, rummaging through crevices with their long barbels. Fish that are forced from their holes by this method are quickly snapped up. The mobs are often accompanied by jacks, which also attack fish flushed out from their cover.

3 RED SEA GOATFISH
Parapeneus forsskali

Up to 28cm (11in). This fish is predominantly white, but the back is greyish-yellow, and there is a bold black dash and a dot along each flank. *Ecology:* It is usually seen singly or in small groups over sandy reefs, where it feeds on benthic invertebrates. It often rests at night on the seabed.

TILEFISH AND REMORAS

Family *Malacanthidae*

The tilefish family are sand-dwelling fish, either burrowing beneath the sand or constructing a large mound of rubble, which they inhabit in pairs.

The remoras are not related to tilefish, but do look and behave a lot like them, so they have been placed in this section for convenience. Remoras live a symbiotic life, attaching themselves to larger fish, such as sharks, Napoleon Wrasses and rays.

1 STRIPED BLANQUILLO or BLUE BLANQUILLO
Malacanthus latovittatus

Up to 45cm (1ft 6in). This striking fish is coloured like an oversized cleanerfish: blue and silver with a broad lateral stripe. The swimming motion is unusual, in that it can abruptly stop, and then reverse a little. *Ecology:* This is the species of tilefish that most Red Sea divers will recognize. They usually live in pairs on sand patches of seaward reefs with medium current. They always appear busy: rummaging in the sand or heading up in to the water column in search of zooplankton.

1 Yellow-fin Goatfish

2 Yellow-saddle Goatfish

3 Red Sea Goatfish

1 Striped Blanquillo

2 FLAGTAIL BLANQUILLO or QUAKERFISH
Malacanthus brevirostris

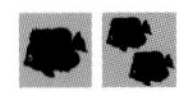   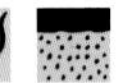

Up to 30cm (1ft). This fish has a pale cigar-shaped body with a blunt head, which is often dappled yellow. The caudal fin has two bold black stripes. *Ecology:* This species is very shy. It resides in pairs on sandy slopes, rushing into burrows as divers or other fish approach. It is widely distributed throughout the Red Sea, but nowhere is it common.

3 STRIPED REMORA or SHARK SUCKER
Echeneis naucrates

Up to 110cm (3ft 7in). The family *Echenidae* is related to the tilefish family only in terms of appearance, being both striped and slim like the Striped Blanquillo. The top of the head is flattened to provide a unique sucking disc, which is used to attach itself to sharks, rays and turtles. *Ecology:* This species is as widespread as the hosts to which it attaches itself. It feeds on parasites of its host, and also on discarded food.

4 WHITE REMORA
Remorina albiscens

Up to 60cm (2ft). Like the Striped Remora, this species is elongated with a flattened sucker on its head. But unlike the Striped Remora, it bears no markings, and is uniformly white in colour. *Ecology:* This species has a wide range of hosts, although it is more commonly found on large rays and sharks than on the smaller species that play host to remoras, such as Napoleon Wrasses and turtles.

ROCK BASSLETS AND FAIRY BASSLETS
Pseudochromidae and *Anthiinae*

The rock basslet family are also known as the eel blennies or dottybacks. They are small elongate fish, which have long, single dorsal fins, and are often brightly coloured. They are solitary reef-dwelling fish that feed on a mixture of zooplankton, small invertebrates and fish. They are hermaphrodites and some species are known to provide parental care to the juveniles through mouth-brooding.

Fairy basslets are also commonly referred to as anthias. They are small, colourful planktivores, which form vast haremic schools that cloak most of the Red Sea's reefs.

1 SUNRISE ROCK BASSLET
Pseudochromis flavivertex

Up to 7cm (3in). This elongate fish is deep blue in colour, with a yellow stripe running down its back. The tail is yellow, and the belly is often pale. *Ecology:* This small solitary fish lives on mixed coral reefs, typically on a small coral head surrounded by sand. It hides in crevices, emerging to feed on zooplankton, or to pounce on small invertebrates.

2 FRIDMAN'S or KING SOLOMON'S ROCK BASSLET
Pseudochromis fridmani

Up to 7cm (3in). This species is small and elongate, and uniformly coloured an extremely intense purple. *Ecology:* The favoured habitat of this species is steep walls or overhangs, where it lives in small colonies, each fish taking its own crevice. It feeds on zooplankton, small invertebrates or fish.

2 Flagtail Blanquillo

3 Striped Remora

4 White Remora

1 Sunrise Rock Basslet

2 Fridman's Rock Basslet

3 RED SEA FAIRY BASSLET or STRIPED ANTHIAS

Pseudanthias taeniatus

  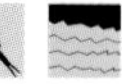

Up to 13cm (5in). The male is basically pink, grading to purple at the head. The belly is white, and a bold white stripe travels the length of the body, distinguishing it from the Jewel Fairy Basslet. The female is pink with a golden back. *Ecology:* This fish forms huge schools, mixed with the Jewel Fairy Basslet, over most of the Red Sea's reefs. It favours coral heads or walls washed with clear water, from which it plucks zooplankton.

4 JEWEL FAIRY BASSLET, GOLDIE or LYRETAIL ANTHIAS

Pseudanthnias squamipinnis

  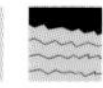

Up to 15cm (6in). The female is orange with a yellow belly, and a pink dash behind the eye. The male is pink, often with buff flanks. The first spine of the dorsal fin forms a long pennant, and the tail is dramatically flared. *Ecology:* This is the species that schools in a thick orange mist over nearly every Red Sea reef, often mixed with the Red Sea Fairy Basslet. The males are territorial and haremic. It feeds on zooplankton and, in turn, is prey to many other species.

BLENNIES

Family *Blennidae*

The *Blennidae* family are small, elongate fish, which differ from gobies and triplefins in having a continuous dorsal fin. They generally live in holes and crevices, around which they guard a small territory. They are a diverse family. The subfamily *Blenninae* are more commonly known as fangblennies and are carnivores. The Cleaner Mimic Blenny is a prime example of this subfamily: it uses its cleanerfish-like appearance to get close enough to larger fish to remove chunks from their fins. In contrast, the Combtooth blennies (*Salarinae*) are herbivores, grazing on algae, especially on the reef flat. One species, the Midas Blenny, even ventures out into the water column to feed on plankton. Although exposed to predators, its golden colour helps it blend in with the surrounding fairy basslets and it gains protection through numbers.

1 ARON'S BLENNY

Escenius aroni

Up to 5.5cm (2in). This small blenny varies in colour from deep gold to beige. Its head is dark with a bluish tinge, and the tail bears a vertical black band. The fins are clear. It can be confused with the Smoothfin Blenny, but it is generally much paler. *Ecology:* This species is widespread throughout the Red Sea, ranging from the shores of the Sinai, where this picture was taken, as far south as Bab el Mandeb. It is a common but shy species, favouring overhangs and the shadier parts of reefs. It feeds on benthic invertebrates.

2 SMOOTHFIN BLENNY

Escenius frontalis

Up to 8cm (3in). In the northern part of the Red Sea, two subspecies are found: one that is all chocolate brown with a white caudal fin, *E. f. nigrovittatus*, and one that is dark with a pale tail, *E. f. albicaudatus*. It is this pale form that can be confused with Aron's Blenny. In the southern Red Sea, there is no such confusion, since only the dark form exists. *Ecology:* The Smoothfin Blenny lives in shallow water among rocks and rubble and is fairly secretive. Its diet includes a wide range of small benthic invertebrates.

3 Red Sea Fairy Basslet

4 Jewel Fairy Basslet

1 Aron's Blenny

2 Smoothfin Blenny

3 MIDAS BLENNY
Escenius midas

  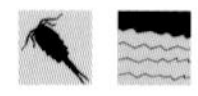

Up to 13cm (5in). The body varies in colour from yellow to pale blue, though the vast majority of individuals are orange. It is unusually long and slim, even for a blenny. *Ecology:* Orange individuals are often seen leaving the safety of the reef, to school alongside fairy basslets, feeding on zooplankton. There, they gain protection from predators by merging into the confusion of the school. They can be distinguished from the basslets by their blunt heads and their wiggling swimming motion.

4 RED SEA BLENNY
Escenius dentex

  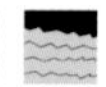

Up to 9cm (3½in). This fish is tan in colour, with rows of dark blotches running backwards from the head, which are replaced with pale blotches towards the tail. The face is pale and two feathered horns project forward from between the eyes. *Ecology:* This shy little blenny can be seen in a wide range of reef environments throughout the Red Sea. It often favours holes in living corals, on which it appears to bask. Its diet includes a wide range of small invertebrates.

5 RED SEA MIMIC BLENNY
Escenius gravieri

Up to 8cm (3in). The head and front half of the body are pale blue, while the tail is yellow. A black line runs nose to tail. It is similar in appearance to the Blackline Sabretooth Blenny, *Meiacanthus nigrolineatus*, but differs in the shape of its head, which is blunter. *Ecology:* By mimicking the Blackline Sabretooth Blenny, in colour and in swimming pattern, this species is afforded some protection from predatory fish, which fear the latter for its venomous fangs. It is a common blenny on shallow sandy reefs, especially those of the Gulf of Aqaba, where this one was photographed.

6 CHESTNUT BLENNY
Cirripectes castaneus

  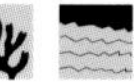

Up to 12.5cm (5in). This species is deep chocolate-brown with red freckles on the face and a red ring around the eye. It sometimes has dark reddish bars on the front half of the body. *Ecology:* This species is found only in very shallow water, in particular on reef edges with strong currents and surge, and for this reason it is not often seen by divers, who rarely venture into such shallow water. Here, it grazes benthic algae, darting under cover when startled.

7 BLOOD-DROP ROCKSKIPPER or RED-SPOTTED BLENNY
Istiblennius chrysospilus

  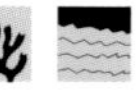

Up to 13cm (5in). The head and shoulders of this blenny are mottled olive-grey, as is the tail. Most of the body, however, is pale grey with bold blood-red markings, making this fish unmistakable. *Ecology:* The Blood-drop Rockskipper is an inhabitant of reef tops, particularly areas exposed to strong surge, where it hides among the stones and corals, grazing on benthic algae. Like other reef-top dwelling blennies, it is not often seen by divers, who rarely venture into such shallow water.

8 STREAM BLENNY
Istiblennius rivulatus

  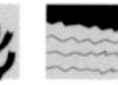

Up to 11cm (4½in). This species has a pale, mottled body with white spots, which are particularly dense around its face. The eyes are prominent, and above them are fleshy horns. *Ecology:* The Stream Blenny favours sandy tidal reef flats. It inhabits small holes, from which it emerges to graze on benthic algae. It is widespread throughout the Red Sea and ranges from the Egyptian coast, where this photograph was taken, to as far south as the Indian Ocean.

3 Midas Blenny

4 Red Sea Blenny

5 Red Sea Mimic Blenny

6 Chestnut Blenny

7 Blood-drop Rockskipper

8 Stream Blenny

9 SCALE-EATER BLENNY or PIANO BLENNY

Plagiotremus tapeinosoma

Up to 14cm (5½in). This species has a white belly, and the dorsal flanks are barred with black, with a single pale stripe from nose to tail. *Ecology:* This fish is similar in habits to the Cleaner Mimic. It is a voracious feeder on the scales and fins of larger fish, and will occasionally even try to take a piece out of a diver. The sensation is akin to a sharp flick.

10 CLEANER MIMIC or MIMIC SABRETOOTH BLENNY

Aspidontus taeniatus

Up to 11cm (4½in). This fish is cream towards the front and blue towards the tail, with a bold black stripe following its lateral line, and extending onto the caudal fin. *Ecology:* This fish not only looks like the Arabian Cleanerfish, *Labroides dimidiatus*, but also copies its swimming motion. This charade allows it to get close enough to larger fish to take a chunk out of their fins, or to tear off a scale. For this reason, it is sometimes seen being chased about the reef by angry parrotfish.

11 LEOPARD BLENNY

Exallias brevis

Up to 15cm (6in). This shy creature is coloured white, with dense black spots towards the front, and dense red spots towards the back. Small branched horns extend upwards from above the large eyes. *Ecology:* This species inhabits the palms of fire corals *Millepora diichotoma* and occasionally *Acropora* species, the polyps of which it feeds on. It is usually found in the shallow surgy waters of exposed reefs, for example those of Tiran or The Brothers islands.

GOBIES

Family *Gobiidae*

The family is characterized by fish with long tapering bodies, blunt heads, bug-eyes and large thick-lipped mouths. They differ from the blennies in that their dorsal fin is not continuous, but in two parts. A number of species form symbiotic relationships, for example Steinitz's Prawngoby, which shares its burrow with the Bulldozer Shrimp. The shrimp, which is almost blind, keeps the burrow in order, in return for having a constant lookout whose movements it senses with its long antennae.

1 WHIP CORAL DWARFGOBY

Bryaninops youngei

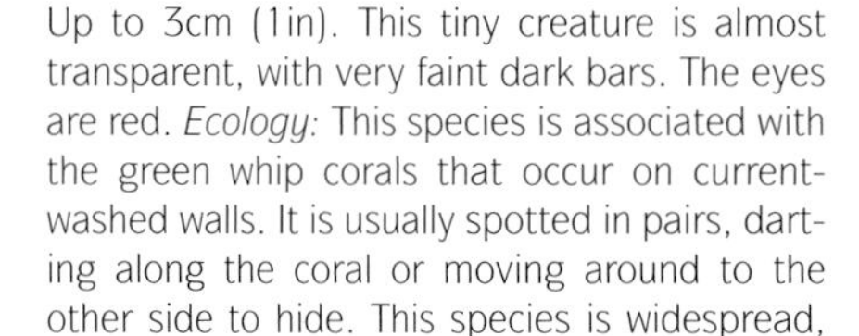

Up to 3cm (1in). This tiny creature is almost transparent, with very faint dark bars. The eyes are red. *Ecology:* This species is associated with the green whip corals that occur on current-washed walls. It is usually spotted in pairs, darting along the coral or moving around to the other side to hide. This species is widespread, although uncommon.

2 GORGONIAN DWARFGOBY

Bryaninops amplus

  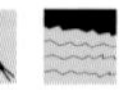

Up to 4cm (1½in). This small semi-transparent fish hugs close to its chosen coral and therefore takes on its colour. This is usually orange, red or pink. *Ecology:* This tiny fish lives on a far greater range of corals than its name suggests. It often frequents gorgonians, but it also favours whip corals, acroporas and even man-made objects, such as buoy-lines.

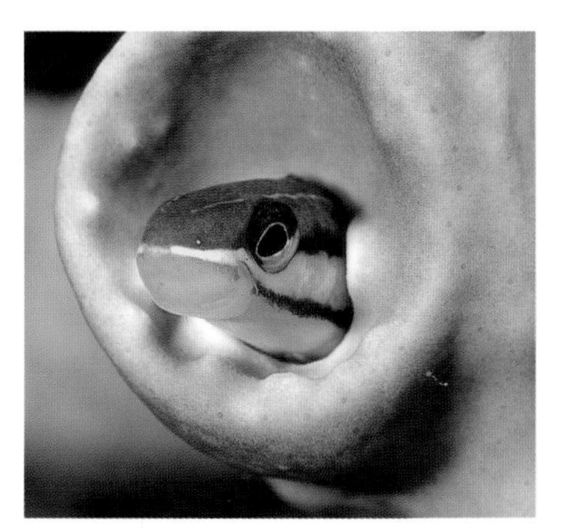

9 Scale-eater Blenny

10 Cleaner Mimic Blenny

11 Leopard Blenny

1 Whip Coral Dwarfgoby

2 Gorgonian Dwarfgoby

3 CITRON GOBY or LEMON CORAL GOBY

Gobiodon citrinus

Up to 6.5cm (2½in). This fish is semi-transparent and bright yellow. Two white or pale blue streaks run down the cheeks, and blue stripes underline the base of the dorsal and anal fins. *Ecology:* This species lives exclusively among the branches of table and staghorn corals. Like other members of the *Gobiodon* genus, this species secretes a toxic mucus to protect it from predation.

4 MAIDEN SLEEPERGOBY

Valenciennea puellaris

Up to 17cm (6½in). The body is white or very pale grey, with numerous orange and blue bars and spots. A faint yellow line follows each flank. *Ecology:* This species favours wide expanses of coarse sand on seaward reefs. It is often seen in pairs or small groups, hovering above the sand and darting into burrows when startled. It seems to be more common in the north than the south, where the Harlequin Prawngoby appears to predominate. It feeds on a wide variety of invertebrates.

5 STEINITZ'S PRAWNGOBY

Ambyleleotris steinitzi

Up to 8cm (3in). The body is pale grey or white with five or six broad, rusty bars. The front of the face is faintly dusky. *Ecology:* This fish shares its burrow with the Pistol Shrimp *Alpheus djeddensis*. The pair favour sandy sections of seaward reefs or lagoons with mild currents. It is equally well distributed in the south and the north. It feeds on a wide variety of invertebrates.

6 HARLEQUIN PRAWNGOBY

Cryptocentrus caeruleopunctatus

  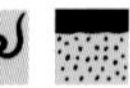

Up to 13cm (5in). This is one of the most striking species of goby. The body is pale with dark bands and light blue spots. The face and dorsal fins carry large, blue-ringed, red blotches, and the bulbous eyes are located on the top of the head. *Ecology:* This fish is widely distributed in the Red Sea, but is far more predominant in the south than the north. Broad expanses of coarse current-washed sand are the ideal location for this species. Like other prawngobies, it shares its hole with a Pistol Shrimp.

7 BLACKFIN DARTFISH or SCISSORTAIL DARTGOBY

Ptereleotris evides

  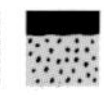

Up to 14cm (5½in). This striking fish is white with a black tail. The black anal and dorsal fins are broad and the black caudal fin is dramatically forked. *Ecology:* Dartfish tend to hover in open water above sandy seaward reefs, where they feed on zooplankton. When alarmed, they dart back down into a burrow in the sand for cover. There are three other species of dartfish in the Red Sea but they are all quite rare.

OTHER REEF SPECIES

1 SIX-STRIPED SOAPFISH

Grammistes sexlineatus

Up to 25cm (10in). The body is grouper-like, although the head profile is steeper. It is chocolate brown, striped with pale-yellow or white. In older individuals, these lines may become broken up into a series of short dashes. *Ecology:* This is a shallow-water fish, usually found lurking in caves and crevices near the reef top. Its name derives from its slippery skin, which has a thick layer of mucus, laced with the toxin grammistin. It is a solitary predator of fish and crustaceans.

3 Citron Goby

4 Maiden Sleepergoby

5 Steinitz's Prawngoby

6 Harlequin Prawngoby

7 Blackfin Dartfish

1 Six-striped Soapfish

HARD CORALS

To many divers, coral is just something that sits on the bottom doing nothing much at all, occasionally snapping off when carelessly trodden on. But if studied more closely it comes to life, and even the most cynical diver will be hard-pressed to deny it has certain charm. The form of hard corals varies wildly according to a wide range of environmental factors. Closely related species can look very different, just as very different species can look similar. Only at a microscopic level can concrete distinctions be made. For this reason more than any other, hard corals have partly resisted man's attempts to impose order on them. The groupings below go some way to explaining the relationship between them.

ACROPORIDAE

1 ELKHORN CORAL

Acropora cytherea

Colonies of this species form flat tables several metres wide, which are thin and intricately structured. Unlike Table Coral, *A. clathrata*, the branches project upwards. They are pale brown or green and the polyps are frequently extended by day. This species also forms elkhorn-shaped colonies, with palms stretching upwards. *Ecology:* This is the classic table coral found on current-washed plateaus throughout the Red Sea. In some locations (Ras Abu Soma or Ras Umm Hesiwa in Safaga) it dominates the reef slope. In Egypt, the largest tables grow on southern plateaus, where they are protected from the prevailing northern swells. After the Red Sea's infrequent 'fifteen-year' southerly storms, they are often found uprooted by the surge.

2 *ACROPORA HUMILIS*

This species is characterized by clumps of finger-like branches rising vertically from a basal plate. Each finger is about 3cm (1in) wide, and tapers to a final, axial corallite 5mm (¼in) wide. In shallow exposed water, these fingers are quite stubby, but in deeper water they grow longer. *Ecology:* This species is usually found on the reef crest, where its thick branches can withstand the pressure of the surf. It sometimes forms large monospecific stands like that shown in the picture.

3 *ACROPORA VALENCIENNESI*

This species forms tables that are loosely branched and reach up to 2m (6ft 7in) in diameter. The branches are less inclined to fuse than those of other table corals and they never develop into solid sheets. There are no vertical branches, although the ends of the branches typically curve upwards. *Ecology:* Like Table Coral and Elkhorn Coral, this species favours sheltered, well-lit areas. It is therefore usually found on flat, lee-side reefs between 5 and 20m (15 and 65ft).

4 *ACROPORA HEMIPRICHII*

This coral can form large monospecific carpets, with crowded branches. The branches are covered with swollen, bead-shaped corallites, which are arranged in rows on the younger branches, and are irregular on the older branches. *Ecology:* This *Acropora* forms its most extensive stands on shallow, exposed fringing reefs, or on outer patch reefs.

5 *MONTIPORA TUBERCULOSA*

Colonies of this species are encrusting or form thin foliacious plates, which are usually dark brown with pale margins. It is easily confused with members of the genera *Echinopora*, *Oxypora*, *Echinophyllia* or *Mycedium*. *Ecology:* This is a fairly uncommon species in the Red Sea, favouring sheltered reef slopes. It seems capable of coping with poorly-lit conditions, which gives it an edge in more turbid waters.

POCILLOPORIDAE

1 *POCILLOPORA DAMICORNIS*

The branches of this species intergrade with each other, forming small, bushy clumps. Like *P. verrucosa*, these vary according to conditions. In exposed environments such as in the surge-zone, the branches are thick, while in sheltered conditions they are thin and widely spaced. The white calcareous base is covered in a fuzz of polyps, which can be green, brown or pink. *Ecology:* This is a common species, tolerant of a wide range of habitats, from jetties to mangrove swamps.

1 Elkhorn Coral

2 *Acropora humilis*

3 *Acropora valenciennesi*

4 *Acropora hemiprichii (right)*

5 *Montipora tuberculosa*

1 *Pocillopora damicornis*

2 STYLOPHORA PISTILLATA

The branches are generally short, radiating outwards with fat, club-like ends. Colonies are uniformly pink, green, cream or blue and the polyps are only extended at night. *Ecology:* As a tramp species, larvae attach themselves to floating flotsam, growing into colonies several centimetres across. These colonies can be carried thousands of kilometres, spawning as they go. On the reef, it favours shallow areas with strong wave action.

PORITIDAE

1 PORITES LUTEA

Corals of the genus *Porites* form some of the largest of all coral colonies. They may be up to 8m (26ft) high, and nearly 1,000 years old, and as such are among the oldest forms of animal life. *P. lutea* is typical of the massive species of *Porites*, forming large, smooth, helmet-shaped colonies. It varies in colour from pale green to cream or yellow. *Ecology:* This species is very common throughout the Red Sea. It is found on most reefs, but grows to its most dramatic proportions in current-washed channels or plateaus.

2 GONIOPORA COLUMNA

Goniopora species are usually found in turbid sheltered water, for example at the edges of lagoons. They are an aggressive species, and their polyps attack neighbouring corals. For this reason, they are usually found in large stands, dominating the reef to the exclusion of all other species. *G. columna* is no exception. It forms tall columns, which are apparently dead at the bottom, with a flourish of growth toward the top. *Ecology:* It is widely distributed in the Red Sea.

3 DAISY CORAL

Goniopora spp.

There are 20–30 species in this group, of which *G. planulata* grows to the greatest dimensions. This species has the appearance of a soft coral, with its tentacles growing up to 10cm (4in) long, topped with a flower-like head. These heads are composed of 24 smaller tentacles. Coloration is usually grey, beige or pale brown, and the inside of the 'floret' is often tinted yellow or green. *Ecology:* This species favours sites with strong current, down to a depth of about 30m (100ft).

FAVIIDAE

1 FAVIA STELLIGERA

Colonies of this species can become quite large hemispherical formations, with nodular projections. They are usually pale yellow or brown in colour. It is similar in appearance to several other species, for example *F. laxa*. *Ecology:* The genus *Favia* is well distributed throughout the world. They are the most common shallow-water genus where *Acropora* species are not present. This species, like most of the genus, is a nocturnal feeder.

2 LOBOPHYLLIA HEMIPRICHII

The corallites may be uniformly grey-green in colour, or have concentric rings of colour repeated in each corallite within the colony. The corallites are tightly packed together, forming a massive dome-shaped structure. *Ecology:* This common species forms monospecific stands on a wide range of reef types.

3 SALAD CORAL

Turbinaria mesenterina

Most species of this genus show various forms according to the depth at which they grow and, therefore, the amount of available light to them. This species is almost always foliaceous, with the leaves densely packed to give the appearance of a cabbage or lettuce. The surfaces of these leaves are pimpled and yellow-green in colour. *Ecology:* Colonies of this species stand alone on mixed hard-coral slopes.

4 MUSHROOM CORAL

Fungia spp.

Mushroom corals are free-living disc-like corals, with central mouths and radiating ridges. They have short fat tentacles, which are only extended at night. This species starts life as a planula larva, which develops into a mushroom-shaped polyp. Eventually, the stalk is undermined by boring organisms, the scar heals and the disc starts its free-living phase. *Ecology:* Since they are not anchored to the reef, species of this genus are easily upset by surge, so they tend to live deeper on the reef, below the surge-zone. They are more common in the southern Red Sea than in the north.

2 *Stylophora pistillata*

1 *Porites lutea*

2 *Goniopora columna (left)*

3 Daisy coral

1 *Favia stelligera*

2 *Lobophyllia hemiprichii*

3 Salad coral

4 Mushroom coral

5 FIRE CORAL

Millepora dichotoma

The genus *Millepora* was once thought to encompass only one species, with differences simply being different growth forms. There are now thought be three separate species. Plate Fire Coral, *M. platyphyla*, is similar to Fire Coral in colour, with yellow-brown colonies fading to white at the edges. But unlike Fire Coral it forms large upright plates. *Ecology*: This species is common in very shallow water with strong currents. It gives a persistent sting when touched, which can be treated with an acidic solution (*see* Dangers of the Reef, p.7).

6 *PLEROGYRA* SPP.

The adult colony is massive, with deep valleys about 1–2cm (½–1in) wide covering the surface. During the day, beige or grey, grape-sized 'vesicles' emerge for photosynthesis. These retract by night into the wide corallites. *Ecology*: A fairly common group that occurs on shallow, sheltered reef slopes. In particular, it prefers steep slopes in turbid, back-reef areas and lagoons.

SOFT CORALS

If the taxonomy of hard corals is surrounded by mystery, then that of soft corals is pure witchcraft. Somehow, this field has defied all attempts to impose order upon it and there are currently few authoritative texts on the subject. For the diver, however, exact scientific details are usually of little consequence. For this reason, the clumsy groupings below should satisfy most.

1 BLACK CORAL

Anthipathes spp.

Antipatharians form large trees, which can grow up to 3m (9ft 10in) high. In the northern Red Sea, greenish-black species predominate, the biggest among them being *A. dichotoma*, while in the south a white species is common, having the appearance of a frost-covered tree. *Ecology:* The black-coral jewellery, which is popular around the world, has led to this genus's extinction in some areas. For this reason, Red Sea experts keep the locations of these corals unpublished. Nevertheless, they are fairly common on deep current-washed walls, especially on the more exposed reefs of Egypt. The frosty-looking species also prefer deep water but inhabit horizontal surfaces rather than walls and are most prolific on seamounts and shoals. Black coral bushes provide a habitat for many other species, such as bivalves, anemones, Longnosed Hawkfish and Diana's Hogfish.

2 *MELITHAEA* SPP.

This group of soft corals are characterized by bushy fans, with thick branches dividing along a common plane. The branches are orange, with a white fuzz when the polyps are extended to feed. There is a wide range of coloration in species of *Melithaea*, caused by factors of the environment and by geographical differences, and this makes identification awkward. *Ecology:* This species occurs in low light conditions, on exposed walls, or at the entrances to caves.

3 GORGONIAN

Subergorgonia spp.

The classic Red Sea gorgonian is *S. hicksoni*, a species that grows up to 2m (6ft 7in) in diameter. It is completely flat, with thin branches dividing and rejoining along a single plane until the very edges, where they are free. Coloration is pale beige, often developing a tinge of pink or orange when the polyps are extended. *Ecology: S. hicksoni* and *S. mollis* generally occur in waters down to 30m (100ft), beyond which point they are replaced by another closely related species. The colonies are always orientated at right angles to the current, allowing the polyps to catch the maximum amount of zooplankton. Gorgonians often play host to bivalves and to crinoids, which become entwined in the branches. They are also the preferred home of several fish species, such as the Longnosed Hawkfish and the Ghost Pipefish.

5 Fire Coral

6 *Plerogyra* sp.

1 Black coral

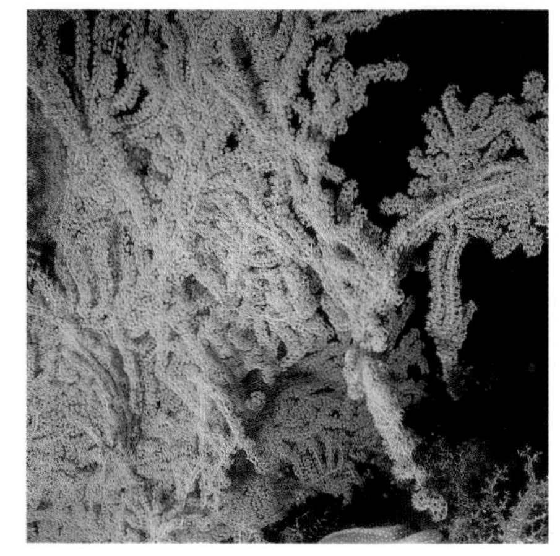

2 *Melithaea* sp.

3 Gorgonian

4 ACABARIAN SEA-FAN

Acabaria spp.

The genus *Acabaria* has about 20 members. Colonies are densely branched within a single plane, and are usually bushier than gorgonians. There is often a degree of connection, with branches fusing to form bridges. The fans are usually red, yellow, pink or orange in colour, and can grow up to 50cm (1ft 8in) in diameter. *A. splendens* is distinguished by the dichotomous branching, the repeated bridging, the bright coloration and by the white polyps that open onto both sides of the fan. *A. erythrea* is generally earthier in colour, and is bushier than *A. splendens*. *A. pulchra* is similar, but is generally much smaller. *Ecology:* Acabarian sea-fans are usually found on steep walls, beneath overhangs or within caves.

5 SEA WHIP

Cirrhipathes spp.

This genus is closely related to the black corals. The various species form long, unbranched colonies, extending outwards from the reef. Colonies may grow up to 3m (9ft 10in) long, and can be straight, undulating or coiled. The predominant Red Sea species is green, but black, grey and brown species also occur. The polyps cannot be retracted, giving the coral a rough barbed appearance. *Ecology:* This is a deep-water genus, rarely found at depths of less than 15m (50ft). It is usually associated with areas of strong current, such as on the walls of channels between reefs, for example in the Tiran Straits.

6 *CLATHRARIA RUBRINOIDES*

This species is characterized by branches of unchanging thickness, which come to a sharp point. These branches divide dichotomously, forming dense bushes, which are either tree-like, or willow-like where the colony is growing on a vertical wall. The bushes can grow well over 50cm (1ft 8in) in diameter and range in colour from yellow to white. During the day, the polyps are extended and they can just be seen with the naked eye. The hard coral, *Seriatopora hystrix,* bears a passing resemblance to this species, but the soft coral is less rigid and generally more colourful. *Ecology:* This species needs plentiful light, so it occurs in extremely shallow water, usually less than 10m (33ft) deep. It also requires sheltered water, as its delicate branches can be harmed by strong surge. This coral is well distributed throughout the Red Sea but is not found anywhere else.

7 *ELISELLA ELONGATA*

This coral has long whip-like arms, but unlike the sea whips, it grows in large clumps. The polyps are usually orange or yellow, distinguishing this species from a similar coral, *Junceella juncea*, which is usually red or violet. *Ecology:* This species prefers steep, current-washed walls, and can exist at considerable depths. It is widespread throughout the Red Sea, ranging from the Tiran Straits in the north, where this photograph was taken, to the straits of Bab El Mandeb in the south.

8 *ELISELLA* SPP.

This species of *Elisella* grows from a single common base, above which it branches out rapidly, with long whip-like arms. It is generally orange or gold in colour. *Ecology*: Colonies of this coral occur in shallow water in shady areas, such as the entrances of caves. The polyps are only active during the night, and are withdrawn by day, giving the branches a smooth, bald appearance.

9 THISTLE CORAL

Dendronephthya spp.

This family includes a wide range of tree-like corals, which are translucent, with polyps clustered in groups at the end of branches extending from the fleshy stem. The coral remains deflated during periods of slack tide, extending to feed as the current picks up. Coloration varies from pink, through orange and red, to purple. *Ecology:* These soft corals are part of a unique group that are entirely vegetarian. They are capable of catching zooplankton, but cannot paralyse them and they soon wriggle free. Instead, they feed on phytoplankton. This strategy means that there is little competition with other corals for resources, since phytoplankton is far more available in reef waters than zooplankton, which is rapidly filtered out by the many hungry corals. These corals occur on steep current-washed walls in areas of clear water. They are widely distributed in the Red Sea, but form their densest swathes in the north.

4 Acabarian sea-fan

5 Sea whip

6 *Clathraria rubrinoides*

7 *Elisella elongata*

8 *Elisella* sp. *(left)*

9 Thistle coral

10 BROCCOLI CORAL

Lithophytum arboreum

This family is very similar to *Dendronephthya*, with groups of polyps arranged at the ends of fleshy branches, but the polyps are less spiky and it is more plant-like in appearance. Coloration is less florid than in *Dendronephthya* and this family is usually beige, cream, brownish or grey. *Ecology:* This group of corals favours the upper 20m (65ft) of exposed current-washed reef slopes, where it often forms large, monospecific swathes, carpeting many metres of reef. It is widespread in the Red Sea, but is more prolific in the north, for example on the shores of Tiran Island, where this photograph was taken.

11 *CHIRONEPHTHYA VARIABILIS*

This species falls somewhere between *Nephthea* and *Dendronephthya* in appearance. It has the bright colours of *Dendronephthya*, but is not as spiky, its polyps being grouped similarly to those of *Nephthea*. It is generally larger than the other two groups, growing to about 1m (3ft 3in). *Ecology:* This species is well distributed, although it is uncommon in the Red Sea. It favours steep walls, with a fair exposure to current, but does not form the large monospecific carpets that the other two groups do.

12 *SARCOPHYTON* SPP.

Species belonging to this group are very difficult to tell apart, but they are all mushroom-shaped colonies with wide convoluted tops, and broad feet that attach to the coral reef. The polyps are often extended during the daytime and when retracted leave the coral with a bald appearance. Difficulties in identification arise because the length of the polyps can be affected by changing light levels, while the overall shape of the colony can be influenced by current. Coloration in this group varies between yellow, green and beige. *S. trocheliophorum* is the species that grows to the largest size, and it can reach 50cm (1ft 8in) in height. *Ecology:* This is generally a shallow-water species, and is usually found in the 10–15m (30–50ft) depth range. It can occasionally form dense, monospecific stands, taking over many square metres of reef, but it is more often found singly. Each coral starts life as a transparent *Coeloplana* medusa, about 3cm (1in) wide, which feeds on zooplankton using long tentacles.

13 LOBED SOFT CORAL

Sinularia spp.

Species of *Sinularia* vary widely in growth form, but they are generally either low-creeping colonies or erect tree-like colonies with fleshy stalks. The species *S. flexibilis* is one such arborescent coral. Its surfaces are generally rubbery and slimy to the touch, with ridges, pimples and lobes. Some species can form large monospecific colonies, covering many metres of reef and, in this case, they are easily confused with leather corals of the genus *Lobophytum*. Coloration is generally brown, grey, or blue-green. The polyps are usually retracted during the day but are extended at night, and are just about visible to the naked eye. *Ecology:* This group is generally found in current-washed channels with good exposure to light, down to a depth of about 30m (100ft). They are well distributed throughout the Red Sea, ranging as far north as the Gulf of Aqaba.

14 *XENIA FARAUNENSIS*

To date, 25 different species of the family *Xenia* have been recorded. Adult colonies of this species can grow up to 9cm (3½in) high, and vary in colour between beige, brown and reddish brown. There is little or no pulsation of the 'florets'. *Ecology:* This species has so far only been reported from the northern and central Red Sea, for example at Fara'un Island in the Gulf of Aqaba, where it was first identified. It generally occurs on well-lit reef slopes down to a depth of around 30m (100ft).

10 Broccoli Coral

11 *Chironephthya variabilis*

12 *Sarcophyton* sp.

13 Lobed Soft Coral

14 *Xenia faraunensis*

GLOSSARY

Barbel: a fleshy protuberance from the chin or snout.
Basal plate: a hard plate at the base of some corals from which individual stalks or branches grow.
Benthic: bottom dwelling.
Caudal peduncle: the narrow heavily armoured section that occurs in some fish between the caudal fin and the body.
Corallite: the calcium carbonate wall that coral polyps build around themselves for protection.
Drop-off: the point at which a submarine plateau gives way to a deeper wall.
Papilla: a fleshy protuberance on the snout of some fish.
Phytoplankton: plankton that live by photosynthesis.
Polyp: the individual animals that form a coral colony.
Pre-opercular spine: a chitinous spike that grows on the gill flaps of some species.
Reef flat: the horizontal part of the reef that usually lies only a few metres from the surface.
Scute: thick horny plates on the caudal peduncle of some fish.
Septum: the calcium ridges within a corallite that form a framework around the many branches of the polyp's stomach.
Setae: bristles.
Submarginal: usually refers to colouration just inside the margin of the fin.
Surge-channel: a deep groove formed in the upper reef by wave action.
Tidal flats: the part of the reef flat that falls in the intertidal zone.
Tramp species: invertebrate species that attach themselves to floating driftwood to aid distribution.
Zooplankton: larger carnivorous plankton.

INDEX